Valerie Owens

A story of a woman who finds

homelessness

where and when she least expects it.

AMERICA HUH!
I'M GOING HOME

1

America Huh! I'm Going Home

Valerie Owens

AMERICA HUH! I'M GOING HOME

DISCARDED

A true story

3

America Huh! I'm Going Home

Valerie Owens

AMERICA HUH! I'M GOING HOME

A Thornbird Book

PUBLISHING HISTORY

Manufactured in the United States of America

Seventh edition published 2009

Published by

Thornbird Publishing

P. O. Box 153

Jenkintown, Pennsylvania 19046

1-267-255-2976

Email address:

ladyjaneowens@hotmail.com

Cover designed by Daniel Vega

Website designed by Parrish Bailey

America Huh! I'm Going Home

Copyright © 1996 by Valerie Owens

Txu776-878

ISBN 978-1-61658-166-4

Valerie Owens

Preface

**While every effort is made to ensure
the accuracy of this book,
typographical and editorial errors
may appear. Your constructive
comments and criticisms are
welcomed.**

Valerie Owens

Valerie Owens
P.O. Box 153
Jenkintown, Pennsylvania 19046
Tel: 1-267-255-2976

Email: ladyjaneowens@hotmail.com

Saint Joseph's University Haub School of Business email: vo235914@sju.edu

Homepage:
www.myspace.com/ladyjaneowens

Website:
www.americahuh.com

Additional copies of this book may be purchased at the above address or you may order through the mail or by email.
Order forms are included inside the back cover of this book.
For additional information on our products and services, please request it at the address, email, homepage, or website above.

Valerie Owens

**To those who are
struggling,**

**To talk about a struggle,
you're likely**

to forget about it.

**To be shown a struggle,
you're likely**

not to forget about it.

**But, to live through a
struggle ---**

you'll understand it.
V.O.

9

America Huh! I'm Going Home

Valerie Owens

AUTHOR'S NOTE

Seeing the movie "Not Without My Daughter," made all my memories about my trip to Nigeria, Africa resurface again. Like the woman in that film, I experienced the fear of powerlessness. I felt trapped in an unfamiliar world. For the first time in my adult life, I was not in control of my destiny. The global village is not free – though in America we believe this freedom exists because for most Americans this is all they see. I learned that any trip to a country outside of America can change your life, forever, unless you are willing to take desperate chances to get back to the United States again.

America Huh! I'm Going Home

Valerie Owens

AMERICA HUH!
I'M GOING HOME

America Huh! I'm Going Home

Valerie Owens

Chapter 1: Going On
♦♦♦♦♦♦♦

America Huh! I'm Going Home

Valerie Owens

How could I have known that by the time my day to travel to Africa came, my ex-boyfriend Frank Valin and I would be getting back together? Now I just couldn't lose my thousand dollars. And they surely weren't about to refund my money the day before my scheduled flight. Frank should have tried to come back to me sooner. Why should I have wallowed in self-pity and tears over him? Why should I have continued hoping that he might find some value in me and try to make up before I put my "foot to the pedal" full speed ahead getting on with my life? My past broken hearts when I was at Olney High School, Lincoln University, and the now LaSalle University taught

17

me this maneuver. Now here he is, looking so pitiful and sad because I'm going to Nigeria, Africa, for a month without him. I actually started feeling bad that I was going.

"Get, yourself-- together," I said to myself. Frank wasn't full of gloom all those nights I laid in my bed, broken hearted, waiting -- waiting to hear from him. So now, let him wait.

Frank and I kissed goodbye and the car drove off without him. New York, here we come! Darsalena Eze, her sister, and I, we were on our way. Gee, did they have a lot of luggage. We almost could not fit it all in the car. The suitcases were so large; the biggest suitcases I've ever seen. They should have required a "fork lift" to move, all of, their luggage from point A to point B. What in the world did they pack? I packed all my best dresses, accessories, and etcetera. I did not bring one pair of pants along. Definitely, the majority of my things were white in color. After all, it's very hot in Africa and they say white clothes are cooler to wear.

18

Valerie Owens

We were going to be at the university, where Darsalena's uncle was a professor. Huh! The university! And that's all I knew about Nigeria. Darsalena didn't inform me of what to expect. She said many months later, that her husband had told her not to tell me anything about Nigeria. She said he felt that I was just a spoiled American that should learn about the hardships of other people first hand.

Who would believe that a conversation between Darsalena and me, at a Temple University Graduate School dinner, would result in my going with her to her home, Nigeria, Africa? Within months of meeting Darsalena, in the month of December in the year 1988, when I had one semester left to get my Master's Degree, I went to Nigeria. She had asked me to help her finish her research, for her doctorate's degree in sociology, and I said I would. Why not, I wasn't doing anything during our winter break from school? When she asked, I was thirty-one, single, without any children, and free from

19

any other commitments or any relationship.

I was right! At the airport, the airline personnel reported that Darsalena's and her sister's suitcases were too heavy. Darsalena ended up having to pay fees for the extra weight. Did they have people, little people, in the suitcases? Darsalena did have seven young kids all of whom were below their teenage years. Maybe she didn't have the thousand-dollar round trip fare for a few of them and it was cheaper for them to travel in the luggage compartment. It wouldn't be the first time someone tried to pull off something like that. I couldn't wait to see what she had in those suitcases. But, I would have to wait for a while since we were being rushed away because our flight was preparing to leave.

After the flight attendant called out specific rows that could board the plane, a commotion broke out. People ignored her instructions. "It was every man for him-self!" No lie every person with a ticket crowded into the doorway of the aircraft. The people were pushing and shoving. I was waiting for the kicking and biting to start. Nobody wanted to wait for their turn. They all wanted to be first going into the airplane. The airline personnel attempted to restore order and to get some cooperation from the passengers. They made everyone wait in the doorway of the aircraft for about twenty minutes before anyone was allowed to enter the airplane. Everyone was all crowded and bunched together. But, the passengers would not cooperate.

In frustration, the airline personnel let the "rioters" board. It was embarrassing! Still it got worse! By the time we got to our assigned seats, someone had filled all of the overhead compartments on the plane, at our seats, with bags and things. Darsalena, her sister, and I, all ended up with carry-on luggage we had to put under our seats and under our feet, literally. It was awfully uncomfortable sitting, for about twelve hours straight, with our knees up to our chests. I mean no comfort at all. Others must have experienced the same irritation because out of nowhere one person started yelling at another something about, "Your mother."

I thought they were going to punch each other out. Imagine a whole plane full of Black folks acting rude, inconsiderate, and on top of that, having the nerve to be arrogant as well. I hoped for goodness sake that the air flight team wasn't Black. It would be something else for the cockpit crew to be operating the plane and fighting with each other at the same time. I worried.

I imagined that if the cockpit crew ended up fighting and we crashed, it would happen so fast that we wouldn't know what happened let alone have a chance to feel upset about the situation. Oh what the heck, we're in the air now. They say, "What you don't know won't hurt you."

This was the longest flight I have ever taken. Twelve hours in the air, straight over the Atlantic Ocean with not even an island midway in which to make an emergency landing on. I got a little frightened by this thought. I decided to try to read, through my, groggy, eyes as a Dramamine (a motion sickness pill) addict, the book I brought along. It was no wonder that I didn't feel the air motion sickness. Shucks, you didn't feel anything after Dramamine went to work because I was sleep most of the time.

It always took me almost a full day not to feel the effects of those little powerful pink and white "babies" about two dollars each. They price them so high! And don't get caught without them and have to purchase them at the airport store. They may cost you thirty dollars!

My book, yea, let me get into some reading. A book called "Fear of Flying," just what I needed. I was already scared. Why did I bring this book with me? I know, I thought it would offer some suggestions on dealing with my fear of flying. Boy was I wrong! It turned out to be this story about a married woman who fell in love with another man. I can't keep one man and here's this chick with two men. The story was getting good but I just couldn't keep my eyes opened any longer. Dramamine, here I come or should I say here I go.

When I finally woke up, I didn't know how long I had slept. It had to have been a good little while because my arm had fallen asleep and my neck was cramped. My mouth must have dropped opened because it was dry like the desert I'd see in Africa. Well, I tried to gather my thoughts, but I was still woozy from those pink beauties that kept my stomach settled. I took a look around and most of the folks were asleep. Good! I'm glad all of the fighting finally ended without bloodshed, at least for now anyway.

I made my way to the restroom. Nothing like the relief it brings. Whoever thought of those little comfort zones (i.e., bathrooms on planes, trains, buses, and ships) was

24

a genius. I wondered who it was. Getting to and from my seat was a cinch. This was some smooth flight; it felt as if we weren't even moving at all. Out of the window only darkness could be seen. Maybe we weren't moving, but we were like the earth just dangling in space on its imaginary axis. If the whole earth could do it, then why couldn't we?

Ooh! A little turbulence! I quickly concluded we were still flying after all. How do pilots fly through the air in total darkness? It's amazing! Here come the flight attendants with our food. I'm starved. Anything right now would taste like filet mignon. I don't even know why I said that. Do I even know what filet mignon tastes like, please? Whatever the flight attendants were serving, I wanted it. And anybody that didn't want their food, I would have taken their food as well. No such fortune! People were eating their stuff like piranhas. I thought I was the only one who had forgotten to fill up my stomach before taking this long journey.

Um! I feel the sleepiness coming again. I'm not going to fight it this time. Sleeping makes the time go quicker anyway. I get so cold though when I'm sleeping. And it certainly didn't help that the plane's thermostat felt like it was set on forty degrees. I know it has been stated that a crowd of Black folks generate heat. They don't generate that much heat. Or, perhaps they have to be fighting to get the "sparks" going. I had on a blouse, jacket, and three blankets and the chill was still "knocking on my door."

Are we landing? Finally, we're here! The Motherland! It was still dark, however, we gained a day coming to Nigeria, what-a-deal. Wait a minute! I don't believe this! The whole lot of passengers fumbled and pushed with the same urgency, rudeness, inconsiderateness, as they showed when they had boarded the plane. I just sat in my seat and waited. Let them get off first, who cares I'm in Africa, the place from

Valerie Owens

whence my ancestors came. This
was such an overwhelming feeling for
me.

Every, Black person, alive,
should try to travel back to where
their ancestors came from, at least
once, in their lifetime. I guarantee
them that their lives would not be the
same again. No, they would not be
the same again. The revelation you
experience is like the account in the
Bible when Eve's and Adam's eyes
had been opened as a result of their
eating the fruit from the tree of life.
Once opened -- your eyes cannot be
closed to the realities you
experienced.

We finally found, all of our,
luggage and we dragged it to be
checked through customs. Finally, I
would know if Darsalena had any of
her kids in her luggage. Nope, only
clothes and, oh, so many canned
goods, soap, toilet paper, Ziploc bags,
underwear, stockings, nightgowns,
Lifesavers, gum, shoes, and etcetera
were in the suitcases. The canned
goods weighed those bags down. It

looked like she had robbed a corner grocery store before we left. Things her relatives wanted I guessed.

The customs officer tore through the luggage belonging to both Darsalena and her sister. They didn't tear through my luggage in the same way they had tore through theirs. What on earth were they looking for? Why couldn't I have been the person carrying it, whatever it was that they were searching for?

We finally got out of the airport and we had landed in Lagos, the capital city of Nigeria. We were in Lagos, on one dark and what would have been a winter night, in December, back in America.

At the airport, Darsalena's sister left us to travel to somewhere else. She had taken most of the luggage with her. Darsalena and I left the airport with one piece of luggage each. Darsalena's sister had planned to meet up with us later on in our journey to the university. Darsalena and I got a taxi. Wow! We were in a taxi just like the ones in America.

Valerie Owens

    We arrived in a place called Ibadan. "What's that smell? It's awful! It's making my stomach sick. What is it?"

    The taxi stopped and Darsalena and I got out. We then had to walk up this steep and wide hill for about a mile, each carrying our one piece of luggage. It was a dirt road and people were crowded together on that road like the people in the million man marches. At the top of the hill we ended up on a street that reminded me of the streets I've seen on the news in places like Cambodia. People were standing on balconies, walking in the streets, and sitting in doorways.

    There was still that awful smell. Didn't anyone notice it but me? Was it me? It couldn't be. I could not believe that missing one day of washing, myself up, would make me smell that bad. Or was it my traveling companion? After all, we both have been unable to wash up since the day before. "Stop it," I said, to myself, "that's just an

29

American stereotype that Africans smell bad." This place looked like a prostitute alley in New Orleans. The women were all half dressed and looking "needy." And, even though it was reaching the late evening hours, it was so hot in Ibadan. Maybe that's why the people were dressed in the way that they were.

We're here? This was it? This was where we were going? It couldn't be! Horrified, I tried to appear undisturbed by what I now saw. This didn't look like a university to me. I shuddered at what I might see next. Why did I have to be right thinking that things would indeed get worse? We walked up some steps into a building. It was dark on the stairwell and I couldn't see the stairs. I stumbled, "Shoot," I hurt my foot. Feet don't fail me now. I may have to make a run, for it, from this place.

We came to a door and I didn't know what or who would be beyond this door we were now standing in front of. If I go by how things looked in this place, "Freddie Kruger" could have lived there.

Oh my goodness, the door was opening. I couldn't even see who was there standing at the door because it was dark inside as well. The time had gotten to the midnight hour so quickly. I thought, "What's the thing about no lights anywhere? Do dark people want to stay in darkness?" I thought that was only in America. Then I suddenly realized that there weren't even any street lights. There was only the light from the moon and stars.

"Boy," was it hot in that place. Steamy! Goodbye central air conditioning. I'm hungry! I'm tired! I don't feel so good! My stomach -- oh! Why was my stomach paining me all of a sudden? I felt sick.

As we walked inside the door to a darkened room, I asked, "Can I use the bathroom please?"

A voice in the dark said, "Sure."

"Well, why are we going outside into the hallway on the other side of the room?" I said. There was no answer given. But then I thought,

31

"Oh, but, at least there is a dim light out here."

Why were so many people hanging around on the steps? Why did they stare at me so? Why did we stop at this door? The bathroom! The bathroom is out here? You got to be kidding! You got to be kidding! Outside! I opened the door -- no light! I didn't want to leave the door opened, even for a little bit, to let the dim light shine in because there were people standing right outside the door. So, I closed the door. Pitch black.

I reached toward the back of this enclosure. Where's the toilet? I couldn't feel the toilet seat and my hand hit the wall. Then I reached toward the left side and I twisted my foot on the edge of some opening in the floor. Where's the toilet? Now, I got to pee badly! I opened the door, a little, for some dim light to come in so I could see. Don't tell me they just pee on the floor in here. Judging from the smell in there, it certainly seemed as if they did just pee onto the floor.

I cracked the door open wider and there was this hole in the floor. It was just a room with no light and with a hole, the size of a large grapefruit, in the floor. Somebody stole the toilet seat out of the bathroom. I couldn't wait any longer. I had been holding my pee for so long by then. Maybe I could aim into the hole like a man does -- "hum mm," some men anyhow.

Suddenly, I could see that my panties were stained. It couldn't be my period! Two weeks early! For twenty years, it has not been two weeks early. It's been two weeks late several times. This told me that the stress and tension, in Ibadan, were already too great. A good thing I brought my pocketbook with me to this "false" bathroom. I was smart enough to carry some sanitary napkins just in case my luggage got lost.

Toilet paper! They took the toilet stool and the toilet paper. Boy, I just did not believe the way things were going. I ended up having to shake my coochy dry and then apply my "diaper." Ouch, the cramps! Please let me make it back to the dark room to sit down, lie down, and die.

Uh, I made it back to where Darsalena was. "Darsalena," I said, "I'm not feeling good at all, could I have some hot tea?"

"There is no tea," said the voice in the dark.

"May I have something to drink so I can take some Anaprox (my pain medication)?"

Again the voice in the dark said, "There is nothing to drink, not even water."

For the first time in my life I struggled to swallow my "horse size" pill using my saliva. How in the world were people able to do that? I tried and tried -- the pill was dissolving and the taste of it was nasty. But, I had to get it in my system pronto. Finally, it was down. I wanted relief to please come soon.

"Can I lay down somewhere,

please?"

The voice in the dark said, "There is no place to lie down." This little room, seven feet by seven feet, was the whole place. Woo me! The pain was getting worse. Darsalena said to lie down where I was sitting. So I tried. Whatever it was that I was sitting on it was lumpy, sunk in and short. Now, I was trying to squeeze myself onto this pseudo piece of furniture. There, I'm on this chair, table, or whatever it was. I thought, "Just let me get through this next twenty-four hours of cramping torture."

There was a knock at the door. When the door opened, I could tell by the voice that a man was standing there. Darsalena and the man spoke in their native tongue. I couldn't understand one word. They could have been talking about me for all I knew. The person came in and walked to the side of the room where I was. He was tall and very dark. He took a seat very near where I was laying. I kept looking at this man and his silhouette reminded me of Shaka Zulu. His presence!

As the daylight began to shine through the window, I could see that this man sat tall and appeared void of any body fat. I began feeling attracted to him just as I was to Shaka Zulu in that movie. In fact I fell in love with the actor who played the character of Shaka Zulu. I wished I could have been with him when his empire was great.

I must have drifted off to sleep for a little while because it was bright daylight shining in the room by the time I looked at this man again. At that point it became obvious that the man, still sitting where he had been from the time he arrived, was no Shaka Zulu. He was more shock -- of ugly. He was ugly, dirty, and filthy. And to think that last night, I was so drawn to this creature. And I had been halfway talking to him almost all through the night trying to get to know him.

"We're leaving now!" "But, we haven't even washed up!" What am I thinking of, there wasn't even a toilet stool or toilet paper in the bathroom? I surely as heck don't remember a sink with running water. Oh, I'll just aim in the hole again and change my diaper.

Well, off we go! Funky I am for sure – after two days now of not washing my body parts off. Yet, as soon as we reached outside, there was that terrible smell again. Please don't let this be the fragrance of the air.

What in the world was all that stuff on the ground? There was garbage, soot, muck, and trash -- everything -- all over the street. It was no wonder that the air stunk so, I thought to myself. Their sewer system was above ground and not like America's, sewer system, which was hidden underneath the ground. Sickening! Who would plan it like this, just to run along the street exposed and where children could end up playing in it like they played in regular dirt (i.e., soil)?

I hoped that things were not

like this everywhere, in Nigeria. Better yet, I hoped that it was just not like this wherever we were going. It was certainly a relief to find out we were leaving Ibadan and Lagos was merely a stopping off place before reaching our final destination. But, before we journeyed on, Darsalena took me to downtown Lagos to the shopping streets and to the telephone company to use a phone to call America.

Once at the telephone company, I had to pay a fee of about fifteen dollars for one minute of calling back to America. Ridiculous! The person at the desk took the telephone number, my money, and motioned for me to take a seat. Darsalena and I sat there and sat there. After about twenty minutes, they called my name and directed me to one of the many phone booths lined up against the wall in the room.

I picked up the receiver and I could hear the line ringing. My mother answered. To hear her voice, I felt flushed with emotions. She said

38

my voice was breaking up. Something like, Hi --ther ---- here --- I'm ----. I ---- you ---. Africa -- so ---ferent --an --erica. Click! The line was cut off with no warning just like that. I prayed that my mother would understand what had happened to the telephone line connection and not worry about me. It was hard enough for her to accept having her only child fly twelve hours away from home in the first place. But, then her only call from me was disconnected from her before our conversation was ever finished.

Our next stop was to the shopping tables and stores in downtown Lagos. It was so crowded in this marketplace. Wall-to-wall people were out there. You couldn't even see the pavement when there was one. Darsalena and I were looking around at the merchandise that they had for sale.

At first, I didn't really see anything I was interested in buying so I didn't purchase anything. Then, much later on, there were these snake skinned pocketbooks I saw on some vendor's table that appealed to me. I bought three of the pocketbooks and a wallet. I purchased a purse for my mother, my Aunt Sadie and me. And the wallet was for my cousin Selena.

Into another taxi we went. We arrived back at the airport where we had left some of our luggage. We gathered it for our next flight out of Lagos on to our continued journey to Imo State, Owerri. The weather was very, very hot there. It was about one hundred and twenty or more degrees easily. The sunlight was shinning very brightly into my eyes. Where are my sunglasses? There that's better.

The next plane was very small. The turbulence was really bad. It was a good thing that I had suffered through my menstrual cramps last night and now today I felt much better. I felt born again. This was the first day of the rest of my life. It wasn't a very long flight. Almost as soon as we were up in the air, we were landing. I was certainly glad to get off that roller coaster.

We went into a small building to get our luggage. But, somehow our luggage ended up on another flight and we had to wait in the airport for it to arrive. While we waited, I began reading from my book "A Fear Of Flying" again. I felt hungry. Wait, but we haven't even eaten anything today. I told Darsalena that I was starving. We then walked outside of the building through a door away from the airport runway. There were some vendors, right outside the airport door, with foods I could not begin to identify or describe. But, Darsalena picked out, for me, this meat on a stick that was similar to shish kabob. It was good! I desired another one, but, I didn't want to appear greedy since she was kind enough to buy it for me.

I should have bought another one of those "meat-on-a-stick" for myself. I had money, but I wasn't thinking. I tried to put it out of my mind and it wasn't long before my

41

mind got focused on something better than food -- a man.

Once we were seated, again, inside this small airport, in walked this guy, dressed elegantly. He was clean, neat, sharp, stunning, etcetera, etcetera. I ripped my eyes away from him so as not to appear to be staring. Occasionally, I glanced up and fortunately he didn't catch me looking. Moments later he approached us and I felt my heart skip a beat. He was coming right over to us. He stopped in front of us. I looked up and so did Darsalena.

He said, "Hello" with the most divine accent I could ever imagine. I remember feeling like I was melting from the sound of his voice.

We said "Hello" back. But, then he began to speak Nigerian to Darsalena for quite awhile.

Then, he said, "Goodbye." Just like that, he was gone as quickly as he had appeared. I felt sad. I couldn't help asking Darsalena what he had talked about. She said that he had informed her that he wanted to see me again and wanted to know where exactly we were journeying to. I smiled, flattered and touched by his interest. But, would he really come to where I would be to see me, just like that? How romantic, I thought. What a gesture!

Our luggage had finally arrived and we gathered up our things and into another taxi we went. On our way some sixty miles on dirt road, we passed by a man on his knees, on the ground, at the back of his car. There was a soldier standing over him with an automatic rifle aimed at his head. I felt uneasy about seeing this and before I could comment our taxi driver was being motioned to stop by another soldier armed with an automatic rifle.

They asked Darsalena to get out of the taxi and directed her to the trunk where just her luggage was taken out. An argument broke out between Darsalena and one of the soldiers. Another soldier came to the back of the taxi where I was still sitting, frightened, but trying hard not to show it. He just stared at me. He said nothing. I said nothing. He just looked and I kept looking straight ahead at the back of the taxi cab driver's head. The taxi cab driver didn't move. He sat still like a statue. So I did the same as he did.

When the soldier walked away, I turned to see what was happening to Darsalena. She was still arguing with the soldier who had opened all her luggage and was throwing her things on the dirt ground. Then the argument stopped. Darsalena began picking up her things and putting the luggage into the trunk again. I wanted to get out of the taxi to help her, but I was scared since I didn't know what was being said. I wanted to just stay still and not somehow aggravate the situation any further. She managed with her luggage without help from anyone and she got back into the taxi.

It had begun to get dark outside. Darsalena instructed the taxi cab driver to turn around and drive us back some miles. Darsalena told me that the army ruled **Nigeria** and they were very corrupt. She said that the soldiers stopped us because they wanted her to pay them money for them not to harass her. And she simply refused to give them any money. Americanized! So, they said we could not journey any further since in Nigeria women were not permitted to travel after dark without a male present. I guess the cab driver didn't count.

We ended up at, (get this), a high rise hotel, a real one. I was happy! We got a room. We took showers and changed our clothes to go down to the hotel restaurant to eat food. Food! I wished my period would go away. How could women manage in military combat with periods? I declared it was a total mystery to me. They must have some real horror stories to tell.

Down in the dining room, menus, with delicious meals listed on them, were handed to us. I wanted steak. Meat! Meat! Meat! It was served with rice and some kind of vegetables. I was told over and over again to drink only bottled water while I was in Nigeria and I made it a point to do that. On this night, at the hotel, I ordered hot tea. No doubt, boiling the water was probably all right.

Served, I began to eat and before I got my first taste of this wonderfully prepared food, that stinky smell was in my nose again. The food had that stench I smelled from Ibadan. My eyes wanted this food and my nose didn't. I battled with holding my breath while I ate. It tasted okay. But it was definitely not as good as that meat we had purchased from the airport vendor though. Then I started wondering what kind of meat did I in fact eat? I better leave that thought alone. Eat and get sleepy -- perfect since I had a bed to get into with crisp white sheets. I didn't want to go any further than this place. Why couldn't this be our destination?

Morning came so fast. It seemed like I didn't even get any

Valerie Owens

sleep. And I don't even remember
getting up in the night to go to the
bathroom like I usually did.   Oh I
wish I could sleep some more;
perhaps for another day or a week
maybe. But, Darsalena urged me to
get ready as they were very strict
with check out time in Nigeria. If you
went over the check out time one
minute, you had to pay for an
additional night on your way out the
door. Of course it wouldn't make
sense to do that if we were not going
to stay another night. So, I rushed to
get dressed.

Another hot and sunny day!
And it would be another long ride in a
taxi cab.   I finally mentioned to
Darsalena that I had not liked
Ibadan. She said most people didn't.
She said that the people there were
known for their filth.

Along the road we traveled, we
passed through several towns that
had only a few buildings. And then
we were back on the open dirt road
for miles and miles. We came to sort
of a city and the cars traveling on the

road were ordered to stop. Some official was passing through and for security reasons, only his car was allowed to drive on the road at any given time. All other people driving had to stop their vehicles. And they had to wait along the sides of the road until the car, with the official in it, had gone down the road – way out of sight.

What a law! In America, stopping traffic like this would be impossible to accomplish, especially in downtown Philadelphia.

Where we had stopped, along the side of the road, there was a huge building that had a fence around it. And posted on its fence was a flyer with black and white print that read AIDS in English and then had all of the rest of the print in Nigerian, I supposed. Whatever language it was in, I couldn't read or understand what the bulk of the flyer was saying.

Finally, we were driving again after being cooked like fried tomatoes in Nigeria's hot sun for about forty minutes. Every day the temperature

48

had been a hundred and some degrees. No wonder many of the Nigerians were so dark skinned. It couldn't be helped with the sun shining so intensely on them all of the time.

The next place we passed through was a little town with its main road at its center. There was a crowd of people standing around there. I could not see just what they were doing but the oddest sight was seeing an albino Nigerian standing among so many dark skinned Nigerians. He had absolutely no skin color and his hair was, without any doubt, African in texture. It was strange how genes could affect people.

America Huh! I'm Going Home

Chapter 2: New Standards of Living
◆◆◆◆◆◆◆

America Huh! I'm Going Home

Valerie Owens

This was a long ride. A long ride! I thought, "What kind of taxi bill would this ride generate?" A thousand dollars! Talk about pot holes. The taxi was rocking and rolling and hopping and bumping. I thought surely the taxi would end up falling all apart with its wheels rolling off in every direction and we would be left sitting on the dirt ground. There were high bushes on both sides of the road and I hadn't noticed until now that there had not been any street signs. How was that guy, from the small airport, ever going to find me if he even tried?

Finally, the taxi made a right turn and pulled off the road. The taxi cab driver then drove back into a jungle like area. And we drove back into this grassland madness for about three miles. Then, all of a sudden, the bushes stopped and what remained were sort of a house and about eight or nine hut-like structures. Darsalena said the house was hers and these were her husband's folks. People were coming out from everywhere, children, men and women.

When I got out of the car people said, "Welcome." Darsalena spoke in her native tongue and folks were eagerly helping us to take our luggage out of the taxi. Darsalena paid the taxicab driver and off he sped.

After living all of my life in America, being in Africa, was such an unusual feeling. We were now entering Darsalena's house and I gasped at the sight. Clothes and things were piled up everywhere. It looked like a collection facility for Goodwill. There were piles of clothes, appliances, books, and other things as well. You had to push things aside to walk through the place. It was dark, dirty and dreary. Oh how I longed for the hotel we had just left.

"Stop Val," I said to myself. Everyone doesn't live like some of us do in America. You're in Nigeria now.

Darsalena took me to another junky room that I think would have been a bedroom someday. What sat in the middle of the floor was supposed to be a bed, but, it was high up like a doctor's table and about the same size and width. And it had a sheet over it. Then, once we put things down in that room, she took me into another room that looked like a living room area.

Wouldn't you know I had to pee again? This was something I was trying hard not to have to do since my first revelation there in Nigeria was that of the scarcity of bathrooms. So, I informed Darsalena of my need for a bathroom again. And wouldn't you know after complaining about the bathroom hole in Ibadan, there in Imo State things got worse. She didn't have a bathroom of any sort, not even a hole in the floor. She said I had to go pee outside in the open

and I am saying in the wide open –
outside on the ground.

I told her, "I can't pee outside
on the ground."

She said, "Come on, it's easy."

We went outside and
fortunately it was getting dark. She
squatted and with one hand she
pulled her panties to the side and her
pee just poured out. I was stunned
by the rapid ease at which she
achieved this goal and by the crowd
of people who had gathered around
us to watch me get my first "pee
outside on the ground" lesson.

I felt myself leave my body and
who remained was someone who
now desperately had to pee. In the
squatting position and aided by the
sound of Darsalena's pee pouring out
onto the ground, I closed my eyes
and began to release the pressure
that had been building up for some
time now. Please don't let me get a
bladder infection here for holding my
urine in so long. I didn't do as well as
she did. Hers flowed straight. My
pee was going down the side of my

56

left leg all warm like I was immersing my leg into a warm bath.

It was done. I opened my eyes to see the fifteen or more people just sitting on the ground in front of us watching this "first time in my life" event. No one said a thing. We both got up -- forget washing your hands -- where could you? We went back into the house and during my walk back to the house, the pee stain on my left leg simply dried up. And we just sat back down in the living room.

By this time, it had gotten completely dark outside. Darsalena said that her generator would bring the lights on soon. Until then, we had the light from a black and white television that showed one channel that appeared to be all talking and commentary. Then there was this loud noise. The generator was activated. I thought lights would come on like a baseball field from the loud sound of the generator. But instead, what came on were these bluish lights similar to those in the fly killer lamps I've seen in some restaurants back in America.

What a difference they made. Instead of sitting in the darkness we were sitting in the blue light. They were most definitely not reading lamps. Shucks, they weren't even seeing lamps. Somebody took them for their money on this buy. But, I was feeling really exhausted by then anyway and, right at that moment; I wasn't caring too much about anything.

I told Darsalena I was sleepy and she walked me to that doctor's table and looked through some piles of things and came up with some sheets to put over me. I took off my clothes and, as I had done before our hotel stay, I slept in my underwear.

I awakened to the sun shining in my eyes brightly. I put the clothes I had worn the day before back on. I went to find Darsalena. She was gone. She had explained to me last night before I went to sleep that she had to travel and where she had to go she could not take me. She said a family emergency had come up and

Valerie Owens

since her husband was back in the U.S., she had to step into his shoes to help resolve the problem.

It turned out that her brother-in-law had purchased a car. And unlike the U.S., there was no such thing as car payment plans or even house mortgaging programs here, where we were, in Nigeria. The brother-in-law had paid cash for the car and it turned out that the car he purchased was a stolen car and he was now in prison for the crime.

Also, unlike in America, where a person was considered innocent until proven guilty, in Nigeria a person was considered guilty until they could prove their innocence. Darsalena needed to go to secure legal help for him, right away, as some time had already passed before the news of his detention had gotten to their family.

I didn't think much about being left behind at first, but, with a good night's rest, my mind was clearer and I began to worry about myself being left at Darsalena's house. I hadn't moved my bowels in days, not since I arrived in Nigeria. For some reason, nerves maybe, I really had to go this morning or this afternoon whatever time of day it was. How should I know? We gained a day when we arrived in Nigeria and I didn't adjust my watch to the time difference. Oh, the pressure is on. It must have been something I tried to eat or maybe I'm just "full" and my bowels need room. It was almost seven days now.

But, I thought, "I can't just poop out in the open on the ground." I thought about my mom always telling me how important it was to move your bowels regularly. She said how, if you didn't relieve your bowels, all that stuff inside of you would back up and poison your system and you could die. Now, I wondered -- what was regular? Was regular moving your bowels once a week? Would that do? And it was already a week by this time. Oh man!

I sat in Darsalena's house thinking about what I could do. The sun was shining bright into the window and I found myself just

Valerie Owens

staring at the items Darsalena had brought in her suitcases. And like a flash of lightning, I got it! Somehow I'll poop in one of those large Ziploc bags she brought. The television commercial said once sealed the freshness, but, in my case the odor would be locked in. Now how am I going to do this? Well, I better do it now, I thought, since the faces that usually stared at me through the uncovered windows of Darsalena's house were not present. When they do that, I felt like a caged animal on display or a prisoner being watched by several guards on a suicide alert.

"Never mind about that feeling, the watching faces were not around yet," I said to myself. And I would have to use every ounce of my imagination to pretend that I was on a toilet to pull this off. So, I sat on the edge of the high table bed I slept on. I pulled my panties down. I opened the large Ziploc bag wide and I held it underneath my butt so as to cover the area that sitting on a toilet seat would.

61

Again, I closed my eyes and I kept concentrating on getting this waste out before I killed myself from developing locked bowels. It took awhile. I was praying no one or nothing came to disturb this event. And eventually I relaxed and pretended enough that I was able to release my stool. Done, I grabbed one of the many toilet paper rolls Darsalena had in her opened suitcase and wiped myself well. I felt better. I even felt lighter. I stuffed the toilet tissue in the Ziploc bag and put everything into another bag that you could not see through and took it and threw it in a trash bucket in the room. I thought, if the Ziploc bags really work, there should be no odor permeating from my secret toilet bag.

I rustled through my things to find something to clean my hands off with. To pee and not wash your hands was bad enough. But, for this other stage, I just had to do something to clean my hands. Alcohol! I poured alcohol all over my hands. That should kill any germs.

Valerie Owens

Why didn't I think of that before? I certainly used it to clean my face daily. Why didn't I use it on the rest of me? I knew it was good for external use only, of course.

I dressed in one of my wrinkled up dresses. After all, I wasn't going any place. I went out of doors to sit in the sun. I sat on this block of wood right in the back of Darsalena's house. Like magic, about fifteen people gathered around me. Some of them kept saying "Welcome, welcome." I shook my head up and down. I suddenly realized what a predicament I was really in. Not one of the folks spoke any English that was around me. They could only say the English word, "Welcome."

I said, "Thank you," and a young girl ran off and when she returned she gave me a hot Coca Cola soda in the original glass bottle. I drank it even though it was so hot to drink and it was so hot for me sitting in the sun. We all just sat there for several hours in the hot sun.

I finally said to, myself, semi-audibly, "Whew it's hot." And off that young girl went again and returned with still another hot Coca Cola. Not wanting to offend anyone, I drank it again. I wasn't even thirsty. I was hungry. I didn't want to have to urinate until I was near a toilet again. So, I tried not to make any more sounds while I sat there looking at them looking at me and everything I did.

I had brought my fingernail polish out with me and my book. So, I began polishing my fingernails which had grown long again. They were about an inch and a half in length. I was funky, dirty, and my clothes were a mess. My fingernails were the only glories I had left. I was thinking that if I broke one of my fingernails that would be the straw that would break the camel's back. I would surely have a nervous breakdown.

All of what I was experiencing was so totally unexpected. I was told we would be staying at the university where all modern conveniences were.

64

How did I end up here? Why am I here? I'm not even doing any of the research I agreed to come here to do. Weary, but I finished doing my fingernails. I used British Red, my favorite color, by L'ORE'AL. They looked perfect and I was ready to cry because they were the only things that had turned out right for me. But, since the people from the village were still looking at me, I held my tears back.

This was my first time living with people, for a long period of time that I could not even communicate with due to a language barrier. It was starting to get dark again. Hungry, I went for the door to go into Darsalena's house. I didn't utter a word. I didn't want any more hot Coca Cola.

By the time I reached the table bed I slept on, the familiar eyes were in the windows again. There were no curtains or shades at the windows. I took my dress off, only, and just laid down again. I covered my eyes and began to cry. I must have cried myself to sleep because it was sunny when I opened my eyes again. I felt all stiff. Who lied and said it's better for your back to sleep on a flat, hard surface, like the floor, a board or this table? My back was killing me. My neck and arm hurt. I felt like I had been run over by a truck.

I heard a woman's voice talking close by. It sounded like Darsalena's voice. I sure hoped it was. It was; she was out in the back of her house, on a back porch of sorts, talking to some of her husband's people. We greeted each other and she told me that today we would visit her mother's house and I should get dressed.

Reluctantly, I asked about a place to wash up. Now why would I ask a stupid question like that? Just as I quickly guessed, she said there was no such place. Darsalena said something to one of the people that always seemed to be around us. The next thing I knew a different young girl ran off and she came back with a bucket of water and handed it to me.

Valerie Owens

Imagine that, it was a portable bath. I thanked her and took it into the house to the room in which I had slept.

Suddenly, I realized that although I had the Ivory soap I always traveled with, to use on my sensitive skin, I didn't have a wash cloth or towel. Looking around, I needed something, I thought. I didn't see anything. Soaping my hand, I tried to wash up. It works all right for getting the soap on, but it does nothing for getting it off.

The water was ice cold like it had been refrigerated. As hot as it was in Nigeria everyday – more than a hundred and some degrees, why was this water so cold? It was just my fortune. Now with soap all over my body, I walked around the room looking for something to use as a towel. Heck, I could drip dry, but I can't get all this soap I put on me off with my bare hands. And Ivory soap dries white as snow and dries your skin if it's left on it.

"I know," I thought, "I'll use my

panties to wipe the soap off me and in that way they could be washed and ready to be worn on another day." Boy was I brilliant. They worked. And after a few minutes of standing in the hot air, my body was all dry in no time at all.

I dug into my suitcase for a change of underwear and some other clothes to wear. All of my things had gotten terribly wrinkled. Forgetting just where I was and hearing Darsalena coming back into her house, I asked, "Do you have an iron?" She replied that she did and went to the front door and spoke to someone. I was shocked, a modern convenience. She asked me for the items I wanted ironed and I gave them to her. Through the screened back door, I could see a young girl putting some metal thing into fire and then rubbing it over my clothes. Then she handed my clothes back to Darsalena.

Now I'm not a swearing person, but, my clothes came back looking exactly the same way they did when I handed them to Darsalena to be ironed. I just resolved to myself to pretend that they had been pressed and proceeded to put them on just the way they looked -- wrinkled as prunes.

I changed my shoes and let Darsalena know I was ready to go. We left her husband's people and walked through the high bushes. I could feel so much dirt from the dirt road getting in between my toes. Why did I wear some old sandals, was I mad? So much for getting all washed up and cleaned. After what seemed like several miles, we reached a main dirt road and right across this road was another house like structure with many hut-like structures surrounding it. This was Darsalena's mother's house.

Darsalena's mother greeted us warmly. Just as all the others, she said, "Welcome," to me. I liked Darsalena's mother's house better. It was much neater, cleaner, and brighter. And there was always something special about being in a mother's home. Or maybe I was just homesick for my own mother and found comfort being around Darsalena's mother.

Darsalena's sister was there and we talked some. Funny, in a place like this, Darsalena's sister was real particular about her looks, clothes, her makeup, everything. And today, after visiting with their mother, Darsalena, her sister and I were going to a combined bachelor and bachelorette's party. I didn't even know this -- not that it could change the condition of how wrinkled my clothes looked or anything. Oh, what the heck, no one knew me here anyway.

Back on the road we were off to the party. Darsalena said, unlike in America, the bride and groom, in Nigeria, happily, have a "before the marriage party" together. And when we arrived, it was crowded. And I thought to myself that we didn't even bring a gift or card or anything. But, a little later the bride was on the floor dancing, solo. And people began

70

giving her dollars; so maybe, these were the gifts -- money collected during a dance. I forgot to bring my money; I felt bad about this.

Moments later, after the song ended, the bride-to-be went from table to table greeting her guests, I suppose, and probably thanking them for their gifts. When she came to our table, you know how you look at somebody and they look like someone you know, but, you're in a place that you haven't been before so you dismiss the idea?

But, the bride, she kept looking at me and I kept looking at her. And almost simultaneously we said, "I know you." I asked her if she had ever been to America and she said she had gone to Temple University. We figured it out! We had been in class together at Temple University. This was a big coincidence, that I would travel all the way to Nigeria and meet someone I already knew.

I congratulated her on her forthcoming wedding and apologized for not having a gift for her. She said that was okay. She said she would be happy for me to attend the ceremony anyway. I assured her that I would be there. Although, later on I found out that I didn't have a choice in the matter as Darsalena was the matron of honor in this wedding.

We finally were heading back. It was dark now and to my delight we were staying at Darsalena's mother's house where her sister was also staying. I asked Darsalena, why didn't we stay at her mother's house, period? She told me that because she was married she had to stay where the husband's family lived. What a rule! What if your family lived in Beverly Hills and your husband's family lived in a New York City ghetto? I cringed at the thought of such an economic mismatch. Nevertheless, this night I also slept well.

I think the hundred degrees plus temperature every day was draining and was a type of sleeping medicine. I would sleep well into the afternoon each day, particularly,

72

since there were no alarm clocks to wake me. Hey, I haven't seen a clock since I left America. Amazing, time here is just the light of day and the dark of night. All there was to do, in between, was to take the long, long drives up and down dirt roads with no street lights or street signs.

I've lost track of how many days have passed and I didn't even know what date it was. I'm just going with the flow of things and not getting all uptight about anything anymore; at least I was trying not to. "Que sirrah, sirrah, whatever will be will -- be. The future is not mine to see. Que sir rah, sir rah, whatever will be will -- be."

Today we were going to a birthday party early in the afternoon. Again, we hit the dusty road. It was true, just as she had said to me; the desert dust blew all day long. What she had failed to tell me, though, was that it stained your white clothing with a brownish red color. Why did I bring all my good white clothes? I should have brought army fatigues

73

for this trip. I thought to myself how one of my white dresses cost more than two hundred dollars. I was hopeful that this stuff would wash out with good old Clorox bleach. If it could be gotten out, my mom could do it.

Mom! I was so far away from her, I thought to myself, and I began to feel a little sick to my stomach from this thought. Or, maybe it was the little bit of food I had eaten here that was making my stomach a little sick. It was seasoned so much differently than I was used to. Much of it was seasoned hot and the spices would upset my stomach so.

Here comes the birthday girl Darsalena pointed out to me. The music began to play louder. I looked and to my surprise the birthday girl was a hundred something years old woman smiling from ear to ear. Now, that's a reason to celebrate – the age a hundred something. The age one hundred, period, was something to celebrate.

The place was once again

74

crowded. **Where do all the people come from and how do they find their way around? Familiarity I guess. We got in line to get food. Let's see, I think I have averaged one meal a day. No doubt, I would be weighing less when I returned to America where I was used to a minimum of three square meals a day plus snacks. Not at this place! I haven't even seen a grocery store of any kind. Maybe they grow all of their own food. I guess that was why Darsalena brought so much with her in the way of canned goods and things.**

Now the dancing began. This was the first time I have ever seen tribal dancing that wasn't on a television program. It was an invigorating rhythm. It made me want to jump up and do "some kind of rain dance" or Hootchy-Kootchy dance. Maybe dance like John Belushi did in the movie "The Blues Brothers." I felt like jumping up and screaming, "I see the light," and doing cart wheels onto "center stage," or center dirt I mean. I had

to hold myself still. Oh, I patted my feet and rocked a little, but I did nothing like this music made me feel like doing. No wonder many who have lived among tribes have wanted to remain there. The music draws you so.

In the dark of night we were still out there with the music going. Maybe this was some kind of ritual, I thought. Maybe this was like an American telethon and we would be out there when the sunlight came out again. What the heck, I didn't have anywhere to be.

In the wee hours of the morning, we were riding down the dirt road again. I'm going to sleep well this morning! It was something how you could get a taxicab any time of day or night there without even telephone calls. You just waited by the side of the road and sooner or later one would come by and that was your ride. The fares had to be low. Nobody could afford to pay at the rate we do in America for these distances.

I finally asked Darsalena about her brother-in-law. She said things were not good and she would have to travel again with a lot of money for legal help. I thought we were going to stay at Darsalena's mother's again -- no such fortune. We said our good-byes and we were walking through the bushes to her husband's people's place again. I felt sad. And once there, I went to my table bed and went to sleep.

The next day we went to the wedding and what a wedding! This bride had seven white Mercedes Benz limousines at a humongous church with fourteen bridesmaids and fourteen male attendants. I couldn't believe the extravagance. It turned out that this girl, who I had taken classes with at Temple University in the U.S., was a chief's daughter and they were loaded.

But, I should have known this from a brief visit to one of the bride's relatives' home. Darsalena had taken me there before we went to the bachelor and bachelorette's party. It was huge, with central air conditioning, a butler, maid service, swimming pool, expensive furniture, telephones and bathrooms. Silly me, so overwhelmed by everything I saw, I forgot to even use the bathroom before we left that place.

I, in no way, imagined that my ex-classmate the bride-to-be was well off like that. Why couldn't I have traveled to Nigeria with her? I wanted to leave with her on this day, her wedding day, and go with her on her honeymoon. But, I came with Darsalena and with her I must stay, I suppose.

At the wedding reception, there was a feast of food and drink -- plenty for everyone. At our table there were wedding favors. They were pastel colored nets with Jordan Almonds in them. They were my favorite candy. I was a happy camper. I walked from table to table like a homeless person collecting them from people who said, when asked by me, that they didn't want theirs. I also went to tables where the candy had simply been left. **My pockets were bulging from these candy delights.** I couldn't be happier than a person who had won the lottery for a couple of thousand dollars. Okay, so I was desperate.

I sat back in my seat smiling from ear to ear trying to calm myself. Perhaps these little things would not have excited me so in America. However, here where many things were not easily available, I treasured all that I could find that was desirable to me. But that wasn't much.

Is that Emmanuel, the elegant man from the small airport? It couldn't be! Afar, I could see a guy walking through the wedding guests looking around like he was searching for somebody. He certainly looked like that guy we saw briefly at the airport in Benin City. His eyes met mine and closer he came towards me. I felt my heart skip a beat again when he stood in front of me saying he had been searching for me for two days.

He talked but I had gone numb

from my infatuation over this Emmanuel who had come for me. He came to a wedding for someone he didn't even know. Darsalena came walking over and I heard his voice ask to take me from this place to visit other areas of Nigeria. She agreed with a nod and I felt my body stand up and begin to walk outside into the warm sunlight.

I thought to myself, "Somebody help me please, I think I'm falling in love." Snapped to my senses when we arrived at a car with two other guys sitting in it, I wondered if this situation was safe. I don't know them! Then I thought about where I had to return to after this wedding ceremony and quickly I was ready to take a chance on my safety. Maybe where they took me would be better. And it was indeed, at least at first.

We drove some distance to a small house like structure set out in the middle of nowhere with acres and acres of land surrounding it on all sides. With no knock on the door, the other guys just walked right into the

Valerie Owens

house. **Emmanuel stepped aside for me and let me go in before he did. There was another guy already inside the house!**

I said, "Oh no -- my safety." But, to my relief they all just sat down and began talking and laughing about women mainly. They began to act like some of the men in America – like dogs even. After about an hour they got up and we were off on the road again.

This time we went to a place that reminded me of the small colonial houses sometimes found on the plantations in America, in the south. These however, were divided off into several apartments inside. And we were walking from the car when some girls, three of them, walked by and said, "Hi."

And one stopped and began talking to Emmanuel in their native tongue. I don't know what they said. Emmanuel just told me that the girl was his sister and she said that his mother was looking for him. Knowing his mother was close by was

81

some relief.

We went into one of these buildings up to the second floor and Emmanuel opened the door and there stood, in the living room, his mother. He introduced me to her and his father came from another room and I met him too. They seemed rather stiff. Stiff like my mother has been when I've brought home a white male she was afraid I would date, fall in love with, and marry. Some nerve, at least I was Black.

Thank Almighty God we didn't stay long with his parents and I was so glad of that. But, when we got back outside, we walked down the road a ways and all of a sudden people started yelling something and running all in the same direction down the road. We followed them down there. I was sorry we did.

My first revelation in Nigeria was the scarcity of toilets. My second revelation there was the lack of electricity. What I saw next was my third revelation. I saw a man carrying a little girl across his arms.

Valerie Owens

She looked about three years old. Then, in the ground, I saw this hole that was the size of a grave for a child. The man laid the little girl in the hole. That's it; he just laid her in the hole and people began covering her with dirt. There was no casket or anything else. I asked Emmanuel what had happened to her and his reply was nobody knew why the little girl was dead.

I learned in some places death certificates were not required by law. So you know no autopsy was of any concern. I had a hard time putting this out of my mind. I became very sad and overwhelmed with emotions. We were in the car going somewhere else and I could not focus my thoughts away from what I just saw. I told Emmanuel I felt sick to my stomach. Just as the book, "Men are from Mars and Women are from Venus," says men do, Emmanuel offers not compassion, not a listening ear, but a solution. He said I needed to eat something. Eating was the last thing on my mind. I'm thinking about this little girl lying in a grave feeling cold from being uncovered and exposed to the many lizards I keep seeing running around this place. And I'm scared of them.

We stopped at this building that turned out to be a place to eat. It was getting dark outside now. This restaurant, as I should have expected, was dimly lit. The waitress came over and discussed in their language what they had to eat, I assumed, since I at no time saw a menu. Emmanuel turned to me and said he ordered some chicken and rice for me. Couldn't he see the state my mind was in, isn't it written all over my face, my eyes? I thought about the men in America and their common lack of recognition for this state of mind and I sighed in the disappointment I was so fondly acquainted with.

The food arrived. With the dim light in the place you could hardly see what it was. Chicken! They could tell me anything. I didn't see a wing, breast, leg, or any chicken body part

84

I recognized by sight or feel. I tried to eat it, since when I thought about it, I couldn't remember when I had last eaten something. I had only eaten some of those Jordan Almonds I was hoarding. I didn't want to eat too many of my candies at once. They were my only memory of America that I could hold in my hand. I wanted them to last -- for my dessert, my treat, my joy.

All of a sudden, what light there was went out! Here we were all sitting in complete darkness. No emergency lighting there! I asked Emmanuel, what happened? He said the government controlled the electricity and they could take the service whenever they wanted and that was what they did.

My food became finger/fork food. That's all I could do with it. It was just as well, because my food turned out to be too spicy and just as soon as I swallowed it, my stomach began cramping up as it generally did when the food was too spicy. Some things don't ever change.

We all just sat there for about an hour in the dark. The guys were talking and every once in a while Emmanuel would ask me if I was alright. Alright! I'm thinking yea. I'm just groovy. But, I didn't say that. I merely said, "Yes."

Just as suddenly as they went off, "the lights," I mean the pseudo lights, there were came back on. One was certain to appreciate the "little light" after experiencing when there was none.

Emmanuel paid the bill. I apologized for not being able to finish my food. Now, I was feeling worse than I did when we first came to the restaurant. That's just great!

We were in the car traveling again. Shucks, with the miles we've put in here, we could have driven back to the United States by now; that's if we could drive across water. Water, I thought. All that water between me and America. Hmm! I won't think about it. I'm already feeling bad enough. Good, we're stopping at another place.

86

It was dark out now. With no street lights, the only "real" light out-of-doors or indoors (many times) was the light that shone from the moon and the stars (i.e., when they were out). We were visiting some family Emmanuel knew. They had about twenty kids running all around. The lady of the house offered us something to eat. I was about to decline when Emmanuel said to her to give me something to eat because what I had in the restaurant was too spicy for my stomach. I was thinking, oh no, don't put me on the spot to have to eat this woman's food so as not to offend her for her hospitality.

Well, to my surprise her chicken and rice were good! I don't want to leave here. I've found food I can actually eat and enjoy. I was so grateful that Emmanuel made it possible for me to eat some food again. I was delighted!

After they talked for about an hour, while the kids were still running in and out of the rooms, we got up to leave. Only, I really didn't want to go. The warmth that came from this woman I wanted to continue to enjoy. Why couldn't I have been visiting with her? Sometimes I wish I could send messages to people's minds through mental telepathy. I'd tell her to tell me to stay with her and her family for the duration of my trip. And, after what happened to me next, I wish I had just begged, down on my knees, her to let me stay with her.

We were driving on that good old dirt road again. Where, this time I had no idea? We stopped in front of a building that in the dark looked like some of the aqua blue painted buildings you see in Atlantic City, New Jersey, way down toward the Captain's Stern end of the boardwalk. "Ah, what an ugly color of paint," I always thought.

We all went up to the second floor and into this dreary looking place. No one was there but me, Emmanuel, and the three other guys. Shortly after we arrived, there was a light knock on the door. I was sitting

88

Valerie Owens

in a chair and the guys were all sitting on a sofa. Emmanuel, nervous like, was pacing the floor. He jumped a little at the knock. But, with urgency he went to answer the door. Two older women dressed in African garb walked in. The guys rose up and greeted them as if royalty had just stepped into the room. It wasn't clear to me just who they were. They were too old to be any of the guys' girlfriends, but, too young to be any of their mothers. After all, I had already met Emmanuel's mother.

One of the women had on so much gold, she looked as if she had robbed King Tut's tomb. I sensed that money was in that room then. A strange and uneasy feeling came over me. I tried to dismiss these feelings I was having when the women began asking me things. I became the center of attention.

Why, I thought were these women asking me questions like I was being interviewed by Barbara Walters? I tried to be nice and answer them. But, my wanting to be

89

nice to them subsided when the women began to engage in conversation with the guys in their native tongue. How rude, I thought. And here I was trying to be nice to them by answering all their questions about me, my business, my life -- me. Well, I won't be answering too many more questions, I said to myself. What were they saying that I couldn't hear about?

At this moment, any fantasies I held about marrying someone from another country left me. I couldn't stand my spouse being able to converse, in my face, with someone else and I would not know what the heck he was saying. Forget it!

Oh they are back to me now! I couldn't remember both of the women's names, but, the one now talking to me, her name I remembered; it was Ekwy. Her name was so pretty I thought. She asked me if I wanted some alcoholic drink they now had on the coffee table before them.

I said, "No, I don't drink."

After, they all had a few rounds of drinks, someone had brought out drugs: marijuana, pills, etcetera and etcetera and etcetera. A knapsack of drugs! Now, I could feel panic overcoming me. My first thought was about that movie called, "Midnight Express," and how harsh the laws in foreign countries were for the possession of drugs.

Please help me! I'm innocent! But am I, I thought? After all, I'm sitting right here with them. I felt a desperate need to leave now. I wanted to leave before Emmanuel was given any drugs.

I said to him, "I was tired and ready to get some sleep." At that moment one of the older women and one of the three guys got up and left entering into another room without making a sound. I sensed all those present were very familiar with this apartment we were in. What was this place?

Emmanuel came over to me and took my hand. I grabbed my purse thinking, with relief, that Emmanuel and I were leaving. Only, not by the door we came in. Um! Not at all! He had taken me into a bedroom with very dim lights and just a bed in it. Oh no, I thought to myself, "What have I got myself into now!"

I asked to get some sleep. Did I really expect to be taken a hundred miles back, to the reception place, where Emmanuel had gotten me from? Yes, I did!

I asked him to take me back and he had refused and told me that he had some business to take care of in the morning close to where we were. It seemed reasonable to me, but what if there was some kind of raid on this place through the night? Prison! What if he turns out not to be the gentleman he's been portraying so far? Rape!

I couldn't sleep a wink. I was bracing myself for anything that could happen next. Sometime in the wee hours of the morning, I fell asleep. I awakened and was relieved that I had survived the night without complications. But, just the fear of

Valerie Owens

getting caught in this apartment with these people with all their drugs, I know, was steady on my mind.

Emmanuel and I left on our own. It was goodbye to the rest and we were off in a taxi. We ended up in downtown Port Harcourt, in some building that had travel agents housed in it. Emmanuel was making some travel arrangements to London. Oh, how I wished I could go there. I've always wanted to travel to Europe. I wanted to go anywhere, European. What's wrong with me? Right now, I'd just settle for travel back to the U.S. on the first flight out.

Without thinking, I butted in on Emmanuel's conversation with the lady and asked if she handled travel plans to the U.S. She said that she did. I told her that I would like to go back there on the next flight out. Emmanuel appeared uneasy with my request. But, I was ready to go back to the States.

After the travel agent finished with Emmanuel's plans, she began to work with me on mine. Emmanuel

93

kept saying I should not leave. He said that I should stay. Why, I thought? He's making plans to go to London soon. What difference did it make to him? I ignored his comments and urged the woman to finalize my departing flight. She informed me that the flight to the U.S. only left once a week, on Wednesday evenings and that the next flight she could book me on was in two weeks. I said I'll take it, thinking, if I can last that long. And I paid her the money to cover the fee for changing my flight time and I felt some comfort in knowing I would cut this trip shorter than I had anticipated staying.

I haven't been feeling too good these last few days. It's been about fourteen days since I've had any real food that I could eat and I knew my resistance was low. I started sneezing this morning and by late afternoon, I developed this awful cough. I couldn't help but think about that three year old little girl who died. And I didn't want to get sick in Nigeria.

It's just a cold. I tried to convince myself of this. It was just a cold!

We were on our way now. I figured he would be taking me back to the village where Darsalena's folks lived. I guess he knew where to take me, because I couldn't tell him the first road in which to take. But, I was wrong. We were stopping at a sign that read "something" motel! I couldn't make out the name of it.

It was getting dark again. Emmanuel said we would stay there since he would need the light of day to find where Darsalena's folks lived. Tomorrow he could take me there, he said. I wasn't going to complain because since Emmanuel picked me up, I've been sleeping in a real bed. Although, the sheets, on the last bed I slept in, felt crummy. There had been crumbs on the sheets and in the morning it was obvious the sheets were dirty. And I cringed at the thought of whom I might have been sleeping behind or what for that matter.

But, it was a real bed. Besides, I also had the use of a standard toilet and for me these were pleasures that I was certainly glad I had access to. However, there at a motel, one would assume that things would be even better; at least, one would think anyhow.

We checked in as what? I don't know, "Mr. and Mrs.!" I couldn't understand a word they were saying. Not one!

We walked to the room and to my horror, there was a bed in it, but there was no bathroom. And, before I could scream, Emmanuel suggested I relax, go down the hall and take a nice bath. Oh! He's a "smoothie!" How did he know I would want to take a nice bath? Was that for me or for him, I thought?

Well, I came to terms that if he made any moves on me tonight, I would be ready. I know it's bound to be coming. After all, I've been in his company for several days and nights now. Also, he's planning to take me back to the village tomorrow. Well, tonight would have to be the night. There were no witnesses. And if he said I was his wife, I sure couldn't tell a single soul anything different. There were no words I could utter that anyone here could understand.

Okay, a long bath would buy me some time to think, plan, and ready myself. I took two wash cloths and two towels with me. I always like using one wash cloth for my face and the other for my body. In the way of my personal grooming, it was nice to do something old and familiar to me.

The bathroom was roomy, with dim lights of course. I kept thinking a lizard or some kind of animal would run out. But, I tried to control my worrying and reserve my energy since there may be an even larger animal to deal with back in the motel room. Surely, I could deal with any smaller one in this bathroom. Somehow, though, that thought did not alleviate my fear of rats, lizards, water bugs, roaches, or anything else that might jump out at me in this bathroom.

While I ran the water for my bath, I kept looking around the floor straining my eyes to see if I saw anything moving about. Meanwhile, I turned to lock the bathroom door. For what, I didn't know, because the lock was so flimsy, a child could push the door open. Forget it! All my worrying is going to turn my whole head of hair gray.

Stunned! I stared in the bathtub with disbelief. What in the world! The water was not clear. It was rust or mud or something in the water. It could have even been blood now that I think back on it. But, it was warm, not hot-- just slightly warm. I said I'm getting in this water anyway with the little soap bar they gave me.

That water may have even caused the severe precancerous cells on my cervix, I was later diagnosed with; I don't know. But, then again, it could more likely have been the "Today" sponge that I had started using for a contraceptive. After all, it sat right on the cervix.

Never mind. The fact remains, I bathed in that water like I was lounging at the "Inn of the Dove" couple's club in Cherry Hill, New Jersey. Again, I just pretended. I pretended there were heaps of bubbles all around me with the fragrance of Elizabeth Taylor's Passion perfume. I mean I leaned back and held each leg up one at a time, lathered it, and washed myself like I had my most expensive Victoria's Secret nightgown, robe and slippers waiting for me.

A healthy mind, with fond memories was a wonderful thing to have since you could call upon those memories at any place and at any time you want them. And if you concentrate hard you can almost feel like you're anywhere in time.

I don't know how long I bathed, but I knew I couldn't stay there all night. I started talking to myself. He's a man. You've been with a man before. You were attracted to him. What if he makes a pass? Isn't that a normal thing to expect sooner or later? Yes, I was trying to get myself conditioned to accept this man's advances like any other man's.

I don't know why his being from a different culture, no, it wasn't the different culture that bothered me. It was his ability to speak a different language that spooked me. Also, the comfort he displayed in being in the company of those individuals with all those drugs didn't help either.

I started thinking of all the worse case scenarios that could occur tonight. He could be a pusher and at some point tonight inject me with some addicting drug. He could be a rapist turned on by the resisting woman.

Well, with those two choices, I could only deal with the latter, if he wasn't a murderer too. If I die here, no one would ever know what happened to me. Especially, if all they did there was to dig a grave and put a person in it.

Okay, I got to calm down. Let me think. If he touches me, I'm going to respond like an animal in heat. He'll get no resistance from me. And if he is a rapist and not a murderer, he will be turned off and lose interest in me.

If he's a pusher, all I can do is bite, scream, kick and fight. I don't do drugs and have no interest in starting to use them ever.

A knock on the door startled me. It was Emmanuel asking if I was all right. I said, "Yes." And I told him that I would be out in a few minutes. He mumbled an okay and he was gone.

Well, being the woman of my word, that I am, I got out of the tub. I dried myself off and wrapped myself up in the two towels that I had brought into the bathroom. Naked as a door knob under those towels, I walked back to the room. I laid my washed underwear over a chair. I hoped they'd be dry by the morning. But, if they weren't, it wouldn't be the first time I wore my underwear wet. At least they were clean.

Emmanuel had taken off his shirt and shoes. Wow, what a body! Maybe he would get raped tonight instead. The appearance of strength in a man's chest always reminded me of a Mandingo slave. He undressed to his boxer shorts. They were silk and burgundy in color. What a rich color? How come I hadn't noticed some of this before? Was I paranoid about the drugs around us or was it the lack of light in the room? Well, there weren't any drugs that I could see anywhere now.

I hopped into bed wrapping the sheet around me like a toga. He laid, down next to me with space between us. Off went the light and I waited for whatever was to come.

At first there was silence and stillness. Then Emmanuel spoke. He said with his thick accent, "Valerie, may I kiss you?" What, I thought, he's asking me? What a gentlemen or what an actor? I just didn't care which one he was anymore. His gesture of asking was a turn on. I softly said he could. Then he kissed me and his lips against mine were as soft as rose petals. No chapped lips for him! He kissed with electrifying lips.

I felt his strong muscular arms wrap around me and I began to melt. I began to want this man. I began to want to feel this man's body next to mine. I wanted the sheets and towels between us to be gone. His kiss and holding of me was ecstasy. I wanted him to feel me, rub me. Like Prince sang, I wanted him to "do me baby." And he did.

From every acrobatic position we could think of we were captivated with each other. I remembered thinking, "Wow, I didn't know Nigerians did that." It's funny sometimes how we have preconceptions about people from other cultures and how, many times, our preconceptions are wrong.

Somewhere in the morning we fell asleep. And I woke up happy to be still tucked in Emmanuel's arms. I rolled out of bed for my usual morning walk to the bathroom. It seems that men don't ever have to wake up to go to the bathroom. They just hold and hold with no discomfort until they themselves are ready to get out of bed.

When I returned, Emmanuel said, "Good morning."

I smiled and said, "Good morning" back. He asked if I was hungry, and after our workout last night, you bet, I was starving. I said, "I was hungry."

We dressed and headed to a place to eat. He talked to me about his plans to be away for a few days and how he would be back to see me. I thought it was nice to hear this, but, what are the chances I'd see him again. He's a mystery man to me. I had no way of checking what was true about anything he said. Since I thought this would most likely be the last time I saw Emmanuel, I smiled to put on a brave front. Yet, I didn't want it to be the end. He was so romantic, so warm, caring, affectionate, with his words and with his looks he gave me. I must have

104

Valerie Owens

been losing my mind.

After getting a bite to eat, we were again driving down some dirt road. I began to feel sad. He was leaving me today. He found the place in Owerri where Darsalena's in-laws lived off the dirt road. It was way back within the bush land; that was where the village stood.

He spoke to some of her folks who ran to the taxi and as usual I don't know what they said. He turned to me and said I will be back for you in a few days and he was gone.

Put off by his departure and the awful feelings in my head, I responded to some of Darsalena's in-laws and before I knew it a hot Coca Cola was being placed in my hand. Why, if the water in the bucket I bathed in, there in the village was so ice cold, couldn't they get the sodas chilled?

Frustrated to find Darsalena was not there, I balled up some clothes in my hands and went out the front door and walked toward where

105

Darsalena's mother lived. I knew we had traveled straight through the bushes to an open road and then we walked across the road. It was there that her mother lived.

It was a long walk. I was frightened that something would jump out of the bushes. I started singing to myself to try to ease my fear. I reasoned Darsalena was required to stay where her in-laws lived, not me. I wasn't married to their family. I can go stay where I wanted to stay. I wanted to be where Darsalena's mother was. Even though she could not speak one sentence of English, I wanted to go where she lived.

I finally reached the open dirt road and there just a little way across the road was where Darsalena's mother lived. The front of her house was faced away from the road. Thus, I walked around the house and there was Darsalena's mother sitting on the porch with some kind of pipe in her mouth. She was undressed from her waist to her head and outside. I tried not to change my expression as I was surprised and not sure if I could be in her presence when she was dressed as she was.

I waved, "Hi" and sat down on her step for a long while. Then after about an hour, I'll say, she came and motioned me into her house. I was glad.

I sat down on her sofa and afterwards she sat down in a chair. But this was awkward. She turned on her television set and one channel with a man talking remained on for several hours. I just sat there looking at the man's face and facial expressions with no understanding of anything he was saying.

When, it began to get dark out, Darsalena's mother turned on her lights. They were much better than the blue lighting at Darsalena's house. You could actually see the written word on a piece of paper and it was a good thing because a Nigerian priest arrived at Darsalena's mother's house to conduct a Bible study with her. He could speak

English. What good fortune for me! He was able to communicate to Darsalena's mother that I did not know where Darsalena was and that I wished to stay at her house with her tonight.

He told me she said, "Yes, stay with her." She motioned for me to lie down on the sofa and so I did. I couldn't participate in their conversation so I went to sleep.

To my surprise, by morning Darsalena had come back from her travels. She said her in-laws had told her which direction I had walked off in, alone, yesterday and that she thought I had probably come to her mother's. She said she thought that I apparently figured that maybe I would run into her sister who could speak English. But, Darsalena's sister had not come to her mother's while I was there.

Then like a burst of fire crackers, Darsalena's sister came into the front door fussing about having some argument with her future husband last night and how men

were all dogs. We both tried to calm
her down, but, she was ranting and
raving uncontrollably. I know it
probably sounds materialistic of me
to have said this, but I said, "With the
size of the rock on your engagement
ring, he couldn't be that bad." But,
then I thought, well if the diamond
was real that is. If the diamond was
not real and he had given her a fake
ring, then I stand with Darsalena's
sister, that her future husband was a
dog and a no good scoundrel.

Darsalena called me aside to tell
me we were going to her brother's
house today and that I needed to get
dressed. I was dressed, I thought, in
the same funky clothes I had on
yesterday. What else could I do? I
think I was starting to get a little
depressed now. Where was the
university I was supposed to be
staying at? I should have been able
to stay there even if Darsalena didn't
want to.

Then she walked me out onto
the porch to show me where I could
take a shower. There was a shower

109

outside. I haven't, in all my life, showed my naked body so much out in public view than I had during my last few weeks in Nigeria.

I give up! So what if they can see my butt, pubic hair, breasts; who cares anymore? I am getting depressed! I took a breath and asked for a towel at least. Forget soap! So, Darsalena went back into her mother's house for a towel and when she returned she called some little young girl, a teenager I would guess, over. She talked to her pointing at me. Then Darsalena said she would take care of my clothes.

I thought, oh, more of that "wonderful clothes ironing" I suppose. So, I went back into Darsalena's mother's house to get the clothes I had balled up and brought with me from Darsalena's in-laws' place. I had used them all balled up as a pillow to sleep on last night. Well, I gave the clothes to the young girl and I didn't see where Darsalena had gone.

Anyway, I walked over to the

110

"out in the sunshine" shower and took my clothes off like there wasn't a person in that yard but me. I smiled to see a big bar of soap out there. Pulling the shower "string," I let the "ice cycles" cover my nude body. I gritted my teeth and used the soap with the ice cold water to wash myself. Why didn't the sun help? It certainly was out and it should have had the energy to warm that water.

I was standing in the hot sun washing in front of fifty or more folks looking in at me. I didn't see any of the female Nigerians totally nude here. I don't even know if they have pubic hair. All they showed were breasts out here in the village. I don't mean any harm, but I don't remember seeing any of them taking these outdoor showers either. Were they just for people like me to be tortured by the chill from the cold water and by being stared at like an animal in a zoo cage? Oh man, I am getting depressed!

Oh, my goodness, a lizard just ran by my foot. And in my alarm, I

111

knocked my clothes, which were already dirty, into the puddle of mud I was standing in that came from the delightful shower I was taking. Man! Okay, I'm just going to let these emotions that have started to rise out of me just go. I'm all right I said to myself. I was thinking, let's get back to basics, I'm alive, still, and at least the towel did not fall in the mud as well.

I wrapped myself up to walk pass my attentive audience and back to Darsalena's mother's house carrying my muddy clothes. They can always be cleaned at some point in my life.

When Darsalena turned from talking with her mother in the living room, I asked if there was something, a bag maybe, I could put my "dirty" clothes into. She got up and went to another room and returned with a bag. I dropped my clothes in it and bent down to put the bag near the front door so I wouldn't forget to take them when we left. When I was raising back up, my eyes

Valerie Owens

fell upon my clean clothes that I thought the young teenage girl was going to iron. They were dripping wet hanging on a clothes line adjacent to the outdoor shower I had just left. I didn't even see her washing my clothes. Not that I could have communicated to her to stop in time.

That's fine, now I'm standing here at the front door with not one stitch of clothes besides this towel to wear to Darsalena's brother's house. Do you think he would mind? Nah! Who cares? Wait, I said to myself. I haven't lost my mind yet. I can't go anywhere without some clothes; don't be ridiculous I thought to myself.

So, I calmed down and controlled my voice and went to Darsalena to explain to her what had happened to the clothes I was about to wear. And she saw what had happened to the clothes I just took off, even though, had they not gotten wet and muddy, I would have gladly worn them another day.

Hey, when in Rome, do as the Romans do. I don't have to change my clothes every day like I did in the United States. There's no written law that says you have to. But, I can't walk around with my breasts hanging out, with a towel around my waist and no panties or shoes. I'm not quite there yet. I'm getting close, but not yet.

So, with the saddest eyes, I could muster up, I looked at Darsalena and asked could I get some clothes from her in-laws' place. She said we didn't have time to travel back there and said she'd ask her sister for clothes for me to wear. Oh that's just great! But, I followed her back to the room where her sister was.

As many women do, Darsalena's sister gave me the worse thing she probably had to wear, not the best like I would give to someone to wear. Plus, to make me look even worse, I was wearing a size forty-four wide outfit when my size was a nine/ten. I had to pin, drape and pin some

114

more of this outfit around me. She apologized that she was fresh out of panties to give me.

I walked out of Darsalena's mother's house with two fashionably dressed women. One was a full-figured woman and the other a medium-sized woman. I asked Darsalena for something of hers to wear since my size was closer to hers. And wouldn't you know she only had the clothes on her back with her. Her mother only wore the uncut material she used as a skirt wrapped around her waist and breast for a top; so there was no hope there.

I resolved within myself, I'm somewhere where few people know who I am and I can make it wearing this ridiculous get up. I can do it. I'll pretend I'm pledging a sorority or something. When we got into the taxi to leave, I started biting my lip to keep from laughing at myself. I looked awful and I was outside traveling without any panties on and no stockings. Just air was blowing everywhere. There ought to be a law

America Huh! I'm Going Home

against what I was doing.

We arrived at Darsalena's brother's house, in Benin City, just in time. He was about to leave. He said he had to rush to some airport to pick up his fiancée who was coming home to visit her family today. He said he was already late. I didn't care that he didn't have time to take a look at my clown outfit; I was relieved. He did say, "Hi" and to make myself at home. He should have said, make myself at home alone because just as soon as he left, Darsalena and her sister each said they had somewhere they had to go and neither one could take me with them.

I just shook my head. Where was the university, I thought again and again? Why was this trip like this?

Before Darsalena left, she gave me a walk around in her brother's house. It was still in the process of being built. All that stood constructed was a foyer, a garden in the center of the house, his bedroom, (naturally, with a fiancée and all one

116

Valerie Owens

could certainly understand that his bedroom was a priority), a guest bedroom, a full bathroom, and a gutted out kitchen area.

No food! That's fine with me. Hunger was now my middle name. Nigeria was great for my dieting needs. Why bother counting calories, just don't eat anything at all? I'll be very thin when I return to the States. I'm starved! I felt like crying.

But, I was able to control myself when I was digging in Darsalena's, sister's clothes pocket, and I found a couple of Jordan Almonds in there. She got them from that wedding we all went to and had probably forgotten all about them. I ate them all one by one like I was chewing on steak.

Left alone again, I walked back through Darsalena's brother's house -- more slowly this time. Everything he had was modern; his girl was getting a good catch.

He was a doctor and both he and his fiancée lived in Baltimore, Maryland. This house in Nigeria was

117

for them when they came once a year during the holiday season to visit their families.

It sure must be nice to be set in a good career with one home and able to build another home somewhere else as a spare home. Why can't I meet one of these kinds of guys?

Valerie Owens

Chapter 3: The Mirage Is Over
◆◆◆◆◆◆◆

America Huh! I'm Going Home

Valerie Owens

I want to meet a guy who cared
so much about me he would put me
in a fine new home and take care of
me. No man has ever done anything
for me in the grand fashion I saw
men do in the movies as I was
growing up. I became so fond of
those movie characters. I feel my
depression coming back.

I decided to find something to
do until someone comes back for me,
if anyone ever did. Her brother had a
color television, cable, VCR, tapes,
stereo; he had everything in his
bedroom. The bed looked ever so
inviting. It was neat with this peach
colored linen on it. It looked real
clean.

First, I looked around for a chair
to sit in; however, there was none in
his house. Therefore, I felt he would

121

not mind if I sat on his bed and watched his cable television. He had some magazines and I took one to look at during the commercials. I still couldn't understand anything anybody was saying on the television so you can imagine how well the programs kept my attention. But, his magazines were in English, from the States.

He had nice things. He was neat, not at all like his sisters. He must have gotten his neatness from his mother back in the village. For a moment, I wondered why his mother didn't want to live like her son did. But, she was very old and then I thought maybe she was more comfortable living in a traditional setting.

Perhaps she only liked a few modern conveniences. She had running water, cold, but, it was running water. She had lights, not bright, bright, lights, but not blue lights. She had a running shower, outside in the yard, but a running shower nevertheless. And sometimes she would have on a gray wig that she would take off at any moment in time. I guess she took it off when her head was tired of it. Underneath, her hair would be plaited and gray in color just the same as the wig. A gift from somebody, I would think. I just couldn't imagine Darsalena's mother walking into a store in traditional Nigerian dress and buying a wig. I don't think so.

All my reading was making me sleepy and the sky was now dark outside. I didn't bother to close the blinds at the window located in the wall facing his bed. There was a big full moon shining in. It had a yellowish glow to it and was hypnotic. My eyes switched to the television where the sound of Auld Lang Syne was playing. My golly wow! It was New Year's Eve and I didn't even know it.

Here I sat alone staring in a state of shock. It wasn't that I celebrated holidays or anything. I had long since stopped when at a college seminar I learned many of the

123

negative facts behind holiday celebrations. The St. Valentine's Day massacre; the pilgrims who celebrated Thanksgiving and killed the Indians; the satanic worship related to Halloween; and the Christmas day that wasn't even Christ Jesus' birthday and so on. It was the fact that I was so far away from home and so alone that really hit me.

I stared at the moon realizing that it was the very same moon that was shining over my mother. I began to cry. She told me not to travel here. No exceptions, this had been a trip I was sorry I made. Crying, I soon fell asleep.

In my sleep, I began to itch and scratch and itch and scratch until it woke me completely from my sleep. In the dark, I thought I felt something crawling on me. I snapped on the ceiling lights and to my horror, there were ants all over me. With urgency, I ran from the room into the bathroom. I had no regard for the fact that Darsalena's brother could have returned home at anytime or for the fact that I had no towel or change of clothes with me.

I jumped into his shower to get the ants off of me. My hair itched, everything itched. The thought that bugs, thousands of bugs were crawling all over me made me sick. How in the world did Darsalena's brother sleep in that bed? Wouldn't you know someone was coming back into the house? Here I am butt naked with my clothes trailing from the bedroom to the bathroom and no towel in sight.

I called out, "Who is it?" Sure, why wouldn't it be her brother? After all it was his house. I yelled through the door what had happened to me. He was very apologetic and said that the ants were a problem in his new house, and that he hasn't been able to resolve the problem so far. I asked if he had a shirt and shorts I could wear so I could wash out my clothes which I, hoped, would be dried by tomorrow sometime.

It was now about three o'clock a.m. Where were Darsalena and her sister? They were probably out celebrating the New Year somewhere. Just as quickly as this thought crossed my mind, in came, both of them, obviously strong with drink.

I'm hungry, thirsty, recovering from an ant attack and they were all full of glee. At the next moment, Darsalena knocked on the bathroom door to hand me clothes. Imagine how this looked, especially since I just met her brother and Darsalena had told me he was engaged.

When I emerged from the bathroom I was full of explanations. I told Darsalena and her sister about the ants attacking me in their brother's bed. Oh that didn't sound right, I thought.

"I mean, I was here alone," I emphasized, "and I fell asleep on your brother's bed. You see, I was watching television and reading, everyone had gone and I felt homesick, alone and after crying I fell fast asleep. And then there were all these ants that attacked me. I was frantic! I can't stand bugs! I ran to shower because I was itching all over. Without thinking, I left a trail of my clothes from your brother's bedroom and I neglected to think about getting something to put on after I showered."

"Then your brother came in and I told him what had happened to me and asked if he had something I could wear. I wanted to wash my clothes out." I don't know if they believed me or not, but, that's what happened to me.

Darsalena and her sister were both "gay and giddy," acting as if they'd been drinking all night. Yea, it's New Year's Eve. They obviously weren't thinking anything about me. Surprisingly, then the brother's phone rang. He was talking first calmly and then argumentatively. I wondered what was wrong so I asked Darsalena. She said his fiancée was here in the country, still waiting at the airport. And she was jealous of the fact that an American woman, me, was staying at his house.

I said, "But I thought that's who he went to pick up from the airport?"

Darsalena replied, "He didn't make it there for her."

I thought, "Oh no!" This looks bad, really bad. I thought, but he wasn't with me. But, who would believe me now!

Darsalena, her sister, and I went to her brother's second bedroom to prepare for bed. We all crowded in a regular size bed with barely breathing room between us. I couldn't sleep. I kept thinking about those ants on me, here, in this house. Like hocus pocus, maybe they would attack Darsalena and her sister instead of me this time. Then I thought not with that strong, stinky, alcoholic breath they had. No doubt, all the ants would probably run over to me. They could blow flames; the smell was so strong. Their stinky breath was another reason I couldn't sleep. Plus, I was hungry! Still another reason developed. I could hear knocking on the front door. Hard knocking! Steady and strong!

128

Darsalena and her sister were out like a light. They were unconscious by now.

Moments later, I heard Darsalena's brother fussing with some female about something for a long while. Naturally, I couldn't understand a thing they said. Then the door slammed shut. It was almost light out and soon after which, from shear extreme exhaustion or perhaps starvation, I fell out. I was asleep in my own unconscious state brought on, probably, from the alcohol fumes that filled the whole room. The window in the room was shut tight since, get this, Darsalena's brother had central air conditioning.

By late morning, I felt like I had somebody's hangover. My head was killing me! The sunlight through the window "hurt." Darsalena and her sister both breathing "hurt." All of sudden, Darsalena's brother came yelling in the room as if the house was on fire. Darsalena and her sister jumped up and out of the bed and went running behind their brother right out the front door. I ran right behind them.

Once outside, maybe eight feet away, across the dirt road was a lot with cinder blocks stacked on it. Apparently, a new home was soon to be constructed there. One could see that a crowd of people had gathered among the cinder blocks. Another group of people was dragging a couple of young teenage boys in the dirt toward the first crowd. Everyone was screaming. People began running out from everywhere, adult people, mainly. There was definitely a disturbance going on. And then it happened.

The people began picking up cinder blocks and throwing them on the two boys. They hit them over and over and over and over again. The boys were wailing. It was such an eerie sound. They kept hitting the boys, one right after the other until there was no longer a sound or sign of life in them. I watched this. Everyone watched this. We all watched this.

Valerie Owens

I couldn't move even when I realized I had run outside with just shorts and a bra on. I had forgotten to put a top on in my haste to see this. This is what I ran to see? What in the world had happened? Where were the police? I can still hear the weeping and wailing of those boys in my mind, some twelve years later.

When I finally found my voice, I asked Darsalena why? Why, did they stone those boys to death in front of a crowd of witnesses? The people began walking away. All the yelling and screaming among the crowd had ceased. There was silence. Just me asking, Darsalena, why? Why? Why? Why didn't anyone step in to stop this?

Everyone participated in this stoning of those boys; even I was standing there watching and not saying one thing to help. I was frozen in place standing outside. The bodies were still lying there covered with blood and dirt, lifeless. I could feel my lips asking again, why?

Finally, Darsalena's brother

131

spoke. He said that during the months of December and January, traditionally, people traveled to their villages to visit family. While away from their homes, people hired young boys to sit outside of their homes as security guards. One of the boys would be present twenty-four hours a day. All of the time that the people were away from their homes the boys would be there guarding their homes. A group of boys would take turns posting watch over the houses. One boy per house kept watch.

Darsalena's brother said those two boys, lying over there, had been caught stealing out of a house they were hired to watch over. I said, "What about the police?" He said people don't bother calling the police because they were so corrupt. The people took things into their own hands. He said it was jungle justice.

My fourth revelation in Nigeria was that police protection was a fiction. Jungle justice -- just like that! No trial! My head was throbbing now. I couldn't stop the

132

"wailing" sound in my ears and I couldn't stop the "jungle justice" from replaying over and over in my head. Over and over and over, "jungle justice" played in my head.

Darsalena, her sister and brother were going back into Darsalena's brother's house. I felt my body moving but I don't know if I walked in the house or was led in. In silence, I sat on the edge of the bed we had all slept in. I waited for my turn in the bathroom to get washed up. I couldn't help it, but, I kept walking back to the front door. I kept peeping out of the window to see if the two young boys were still lying there. Where were their parents?

Now, I wanted to go back to the U.S.A. immediately. I wanted to somehow move my departing date up some more. I didn't care if I ever saw the university. I've had enough of Nigeria.

We were leaving. Good! As soon as I could, I would ask to leave to go back to the United States.

Back at Darsalena's house, I asked to leave Nigeria. Her reply was if I wanted to go back to the U.S., I would have to find my own way. A chill went over my body. Was this the new friend I had made and agreed to spend well over two thousand dollars to travel with and to use my time to help finish her research for her dissertation? This couldn't be happening. My feelings were crushed and I excused myself and went to bed without anything to eat. This place was great for my diet. So many meals missed. I had to be losing weight. I haven't seen a full length mirror since our first hotel stay, at the beginning of this trip.

It wasn't even dark out yet. But, I went to lie on the "table bed," staring up at the ceiling. And no, "sugar plums weren't dancing in my head." Night finally came and I was still staring up at the ceiling. My mind kept going back to the little girl buried, not even in a body bag, and the bodies of the teenage boys not even put into a grave. Sleep finally

134

rescued me from my "thinking and remembering" head.

In the morning, when I looked for Darsalena, she was gone from her bed. I looked all around her house -- inside and out. I couldn't find her anywhere. I got dressed and walked again to Darsalena's mother's house. Her mother was there, alone, so I went into the house to sit on her sofa. Surely, she knew by now that I wanted to be at her house instead of at Darsalena's in-laws place.

Several hours later, a rather distinguished looking gentleman walked in. It was Darsalena's uncle from the university. He came to me and asked why we had not shown up at the university. He said he had been waiting there for our arrival. He wanted to know where Darsalena was. I told him I didn't know.

He turned and asked Darsalena's mother, "Where's Darsalena?" She must not have known either because the uncle had clearly gotten angry. He said Darsalena should not have left me in the village like this. He told me to come with him and that there was one place she might be. So he drove me down the road farther than I had been before. We drove quite a distance. Why did I trust this man enough to go with him? Perhaps because he was the only one that seemed to care that I had been left in the village alone among strangers.

Well, the place we ended up at we didn't find Darsalena or her sister. The uncle told me he would drive me to a hotel where I should have been all along until I arrived at the university. He took me to this high rise, modern looking hotel in the middle of what looked like the desert. Nothing but dirt and/or sand was all around the hotel. And I mean nothing.

I told him I didn't have all of my money with me. What was left of it -- that is? But, he said he would take care of the hotel registration for me and I could straighten my finances out with him later. He then said he was going to find Darsalena. We went into the hotel. It was a nice place. It was so clean and so modern. Someone had put a lot of money into this place.

After the uncle spoke to the desk clerk, I was given a key to a room and directed to the elevators. The uncle didn't come up with me, but set out to find his niece. What a gentleman?

On the seventh floor, I found my room and to my surprise and delight there was a little refrigerator in the room. Clean sheets, hot water, a toilet, toilet paper, lights, a blanket, mirrors, a place to hang clothes, a chair to sit in, a sliding glass door window in which to look out and a balcony. I was so excited. I didn't know what to do next.

My stomach growled. Food! I had not eaten a thing. That was what was next -- eating some food. So, I went back down to the lobby before I realized I only had about twenty U.S. dollars on me. All my remaining traveler's checks were locked in my suitcase back at Darsalena's house.

Oh well, maybe I could find something for that price. I asked the hotel employee, I passed in the lobby, where could I get something to eat around here. He said you had to buy your food and bring it to the hotel. Now, I knew what the refrigerator in the hotel rooms was for. That's all well and good, but, how do you cook it or even warm it for that matter. Let me guess. You sit it on your hotel room balcony to warm in the sun. Why not! It was always more than one hundred and ten degrees every day.

Of course, you could prepare your food by lighting a match and presto "flambé'" or "burnt-be'," one or the other. How could somebody construct a magnificent hotel with a casino, pool and forget to construct a restaurant, food store or something? Beats me! Some people just don't need to eat, I suppose. Well, I sure as heck do. I'm going to get me something to eat. I'm tired of going to bed hungry most every night. If hunger hurts like this, I can't imagine

Valerie Owens

how people stay alive while they're starving to death. I'm ready to pass out. My sugar level was so low. I knew my resistance was low too.

I walked out the front door and for miles and miles all I could see was open dirt land. No "green" life anywhere. Just the shrubbery around the hotel -- imported no doubt. I sat outside on one of the lounge chairs near the pool. Out of nowhere, three little Nigerian children, I guessed, came near me while I was deep in thought. And the funniest thing happened. They started pointing at me.

They kept calling me, "White person." "White...person!" They couldn't have been more than five or six years old. I kept telling them. I'm not white. Yea right, like they could understand me. But, how could they? It seems that they couldn't even speak any English, except the words "white person."

Then I thought about it. Well, compared to their deep dark skin tones, even though I was an average

139

light skinned Black person, I did appear white in color, comparatively that is. I could certainly understand their confusion. Imagine that!

I was in a country where all the people I saw were Black. I didn't meet one White person the whole time I was in Nigeria. I don't even remember seeing one. The people, that owned this hotel, were Greeks. How did they find their way over here? And why were they here?

The kids ran away. I could hear a female voice calling out; perhaps she was calling for them. I, at no time, saw her face.

Suddenly, this long tailed lizard ran by my foot. Well, I almost jumped clear into the pool, trying to get out of its way. I can't even swim, and there was no life guard in sight. And, I would be at the deep end of the pool. I caught my balance and quickly got out of the pool area.

Then I noticed some flames at a distance -- way across the street, road, dirt whatever. It smelled like food cooking. But, you know, as hungry as I was, I could have been hallucinating. I said feet don't fail me now, and I walked over where the smell was coming from. There was this Nigerian man cooking some kind of meat over one of those big steel drums or cans. It was rusty and bent. I thought about that meat I had at the little airport we stopped in when Darsalena and I was first coming to this place. It was so good! My mouth began to salivate at the thought of it. I wanted some more.

I took out one of my U.S. dollars which were equal to five naira (Nigerian dollars) at the time. I thought surely this could buy me some of that meat. I pointed the dollar toward the meat and the man shook his head as if he understood what I meant. Who says money doesn't talk?

He put onions on the meat and some kind of sauce; clear sauce, not barbecue sauce or tomato sauce. Just clear sauce with unidentifiable herbs poured over it. Then he grabbed some newspaper.

141

Newspaper? He dumped the meat in it and rolled it up like a subway sandwich. What could I say? What could I do? I had to accept it.

Hence, I gave him the dollar and off I ran back to my hotel room. I hurried like a starved crazed maniac. I opened my door and sat on the chair. As I opened the newspaper, the ink from the print of the paper got all over my hands. So you know it was all over this saucy, greasy, "who-cares-kind-of-meat."

I calmed myself down and convinced myself to limit the ink I was about to eat by at least washing my hands off before I ate. I got one of the towels and tried to wipe some of the ink off of the meat. It was of no use.

I sat right there and ate every "ink print" stained piece of that meat. It was delicious! Fantastic! Probably not very nutritious with the ink on it, but, it satisfied me. I loved it! With a full stomach now, I was ready for a bath. I was ready to relax and gain some composure from this "trip" I

142

was certainly on.

I noticed the bath water was hotter than it had been at the motel that Emmanuel and I had stayed in. The water was even clear. Emmanuel! Hmm! Emmanuel! I wondered where he could be now. He certainly wasn't with me. I felt a little teary eyed. Somehow with him around, I felt sort of protected. But he had gotten my "goods" and gone.

I got out of the tub. I turned on the television set and each channel was blank. I looked at this big old television that sat on the bureau and wondered why it was there? Scenery I guess. Then I looked for a Bible. There wasn't even a Bible in the bureau drawer. I had nothing to do. I had no one to call. I had no one to talk to. So, I called the front desk. I just wanted to hear another human being's voice. I asked what time did the casino close.

The person said, "The casino closes in about two hours." I put my dirty clothes back on. They were all I had. Darsalena's uncle didn't take

143

me for my things I left in the village and I forgot to ask him to.

On my way to the casino, I stopped to talk with the guy at the desk. He could speak pretty good English. I didn't mean to be a bother, but I was so lonely. I wanted to go back to the United States.

I began to tell this man about Emmanuel. Why? I don't know. Somehow, I wanted this man to find him for me. I talked a little about myself too. After an hour went by, I stopped my babbling and told him I was going to the casino before it closed. I had one hour left to win something. I had nineteen U.S. dollars which equaled ninety-five naira (Nigerian dollars). That's not bad. I'll start off with the nickel machines.

I got in there and I was surprised to find that they not only didn't have nickel machines, they didn't even have quarters or half a dollar machines either. They had dollar, five dollars, and ten dollars, I mean, they had five naira, twenty-

144

five naira, and fifty naira machines only. And of course they had the card tables. I didn't play the cards. I played the cheapest thing, the five naira machines.

I don't remember when I ever saw nineteen U.S. dollars (ninety-five naira) go so quickly. I was broke. It was one a.m. when I came in this place and it was now one-o-five a.m. when I left. What a rip off! They just ate my money up. Nobody in there seemed to be winning anything. Not like in Atlantic City, New Jersey, where you often heard the bell ringing when someone had hit the jackpot.

That's what I get. I shouldn't have been in that place gambling away my money anyway. Wasn't being here in Nigeria, alone, not being able to speak the Nigerian language, with my very life at risk, a big enough gamble? What more did I need? Forget what I said. I shuddered at the thought of what more could happen. I was alive, barely; I was clean, mostly; I was fed, some; and I hadn't had a nervous breakdown, I hoped.

On my way back to my room, I stopped at the front desk and asked if I could get a cab out in the middle of nowhere. I told the guy I needed someone to take me back to get my things. He said he knew someone he could call. The hotel desk clerk said it was someone who was like a friend of his that earned his living driving folks around. I told him I didn't know exactly where the place was, but, that I would be willing to pay the driver extra to help me find the place.

The guy at the front desk said he would arrange everything for me for tomorrow. I told him to make it for sometime in the afternoon, about two o'clock, since I had planned to sleep in late. I had to go back to get my things. I had to go back if for nothing more than my little bit of money that was left and my passport. I had to go back to get those things.

What a night! I was freezing all night. I just couldn't get warm. There was no heat in the room. Why would there be when daily the temperature rose well over one hundred and ten degrees easily? Well, it wasn't that temperature outside now. So I wrapped myself up like a ball with the blanket and top sheet on the bed. I put my head underneath the blanket and the top sheet trying to get my hot breath to warm me. It just wasn't working.

I am going to die here. I'm going to freeze to death tonight. I know it!

But, then I remembered I was in a hotel; they've got to have some extra blankets. I called downstairs and the same man answered. I told him I was very cold and wished to have several more blankets. He said he would send some up to me and about fifteen minutes later there was a light knock on my door. I stumbled out of the bed wearing the blanket and top sheet around me.

I asked "Who is it?"

And a low speaking voice said, "Housekeeping with your blankets Miss." I swung the door open as if I had won the Publisher's Clearing House Sweepstakes. I thanked the man three times and closed the door. I didn't have any more money for a tip. I felt bad about that. But, what could I do about it now? I was double-d-broke!

I opened the four blankets sent up to me and laid them over me. I began to feel warm. I fell asleep. It was the best sleep I'd had since I'd been to Nigeria. Every part of me must have been terribly exhausted.

I awakened to the phone ringing in the room. Groggy from sleep, I thought I was back in my apartment in Conshohocken, Pennsylvania, the good old U.S. of A. When I came to my senses, I saw that I was wrong -- wrong -- wrong. I was still here!

I answered the phone. It was the front desk calling to tell me my cab was here. I jumped up, looked at the sunlight in the window and thought I had slept the whole day away. I asked what time was it. The voice on the other end of the phone

148

Valerie Owens

said noon.

My ride was two hours early. I didn't want to miss it. I told the person at the front desk to tell the driver I would be right down. I jumped up and put my same clothes back on and I didn't even wash up. I sure hope this wearing my clothes for days at a time and not washing doesn't develop into a bad habit I can't break when I'm back in the States.

My mother changed my clothes each and every day as I grew up. People have told me she dressed me up like a little doll. I grew up with personal grooming as a vital part of my daily habits, my life. Clean clothes and underwear for each new day. Thank goodness no one really knows me here.

I went down to the lobby and my "cabby" was waiting for me in the lobby. I spoke and told him what I needed to do and about my not really being sure how to find the village I needed to go to. He said we would find it. He seemed very nice. He

even said he was sorry I was not having a nice stay in his country.

We began to drive toward Imo State, Owerri -- I think that was the place. It was a very long ride again and there were a few spots I remembered passing some time before.

On and on we rode. We went around this center monument in the middle of the road, in some town, I had seen before. We were going right so far. He kept driving and I started explaining my circumstances. I said that I was leaving on my own initiative and not in agreement with my host. No doubt her in-laws won't understand what was actually going on with Darsalena and me. I told him no matter what they say, please don't leave me there and please wait to take me back to the hotel.

By the side of the road, I saw Darsalena's mother's house. I told the driver, "Turn right here." He made a right turn and we drove that three miles back into the bushes. We found the place.

Valerie Owens

I pointed toward Darsalena's house and said, "Over there." All of the people in the village came from everywhere -- just running. When my driver stopped the cab, people began yelling at us.

I told the driver, "Please, please, whatever you do, please, don't leave me here. Please don't leave me here."

I jumped out and ran into Darsalena's house and I dragged one of my heavy suitcases out and people were fussing at the driver and he was yelling back at them. I struggled with my suitcase and the people blocked the driver from helping me to lift my suitcase into the cab.

With power from somewhere, fear power probably, I lifted my suitcase and shoved it in. I ran back into Darsalena's house to get my other suitcase and dragged it out too. The driver was able to get by the yelling people and he quickly lifted my other suitcase in for me. I jumped back in and he jumped back in his taxi and we sped off.

A sigh of relief eased the tension I felt all over. I asked him, "What were they saying?" He said they were telling him that he had no right to be in their village and no right to take me away. They wanted to know how he had found their village and he said that I had directed him there. They did not believe that I had found my way to their village.

We were on our way back to the hotel and I for one was glad. When we got there, I asked the driver to wait for me to take my luggage upstairs and I would bring his money back down. Good, his friend was working at the front desk again. I thanked him and they began to talk while I went upstairs.

One of the hotel bellhops took my luggage up for me. Once inside my hotel room, I asked the bellhop to lift one of my suitcases up onto the bed. I quickly unlocked it and got out my remaining money. I gave the bellman a dollar tip (five naira) and thanked him for his services.

I then locked the combination

lock on my suitcase. And then I went back down to the lobby and paid the cab driver twenty U.S. dollars (one hundred naira) for driving me to the village and helping me to escape from there. I thanked him over and over again. I, also, gave the front desk guy five U.S. dollars (twenty-five naira) for arranging everything for me.

If I could last just two more days, I could be in the States by this Thursday. This Thursday! I had my passport and my ticket. I paid for my change in departure time. I'm almost on my way.

I went back upstairs smiling from ear to ear. I got washed up and changed my clothes. Ah, fresh clean clothes. There is nothing like the feeling.

I decided to buy the meat from the man outside cooking again. I went over there to him and this time I greeted him with a smile. I asked him for two orders. I wanted one for now and one for later that night. I even gave him a U.S. dollar tip (five naira) for his services and for his being out there. Ink or no ink – it was some kind of meat to eat. I was having no problem eating and enjoying his food.

When I got back up to my room, having all my things with me, I felt like I used to feel on a Christmas morning. I neatly folded my clothes up and laid them in the drawers. I don't know why, since I would be leaving in two days. Just something to do I guess.

Now, I was ready to eat one of my orders of meat. Yelp! It was wrapped in newspaper again. And again I ate the "ink," meat, onions and delicious sauce with my fingers. This was real finger food.

I took another bath. This time I had my Victoria's Secret lingerie and silk slippers to wear. I had the book I was reading. The house keeper had folded the extra blankets and left them in my room. This hotel stay was probably costing me a fortune, but, I had to stay here to keep what sanity I had left.

Valerie Owens

I still wasn't feeling all that good. I still had an awful cough that hurt my chest each time. I knew I would get sick. I'm not even eating enough. It's hot outside, but, oh so cold in this hotel. Maybe if they'd turn that air conditioner down some, they could afford to build a restaurant in this place or at least a store with medicines, snacks, books, magazines, fingernail polishes and other merchandises.

I thought going to bed early tonight might help my condition. I was wrong. I sneezed and coughed the whole night. I ended up getting very little sleep. By morning, I had a terrible headache. I ate my second order of meat, onions and ink for my breakfast. Maybe I was poisoning myself with this food, but, I needed something to eat. I didn't have any more mint Lifesavers candy, no more Jordan Almonds; I only had this meat. I didn't even think to ask the man at the front desk to maybe bring me some food when he came to work. He was doing so much for me already.

I finally got dressed and went down to the lobby and who should I run into? Darsalena! Her uncle must have caught up with her and told her where I was. She had this middle aged looking guy with her. He was short, chubby and not a bit appealing in his appearance.

For me, it's not just the physical features a man may possess, but, his "polish." The way he wore his clothes, the kind of clothes he wore, the neatness of his hair, groomed nails, the appearance of his teeth, his breath, the trim of his mustache (if he had one), the cologne he wore, and the way he walked.

I don't like men with beards and if he was starting to get a bald head, I'd rather he cut all his hair off and wear a Yul Brynner look instead. I like a man's ears and nose to be clean. I'd like him not to have sleep in his eyes midday. And there's nothing like a man who wears fine shoes with their heels even. No run-down shoes man for me. I don't like a man to fart, openly, once he gets to know me either.

Emmanuel was polished from head to toe. But, this man Darsalena was with was a sight and I don't mean a pleasant one either. Without even asking about me, Darsalena introduced me to the man. She said some name I couldn't even begin to pronounce. She said that he was there to take me out to lunch. To lunch I said, who is he? Why? She went on to tell me that he was a millionaire. I didn't care. I wasn't going anywhere with him. I wasn't going away from this hotel even with Darsalena. She had left me stranded for the last time.

I told her no thanks that I was not interested in having lunch. And I said that I had already eaten, but, thanks for the thought. The man seemed greatly annoyed, irritated even. I don't know what Darsalena said or promised this guy, but, whatever it was, he wasn't happy with my response.

He turned away and walked

toward the front door of the hotel. Talking in her native tongue, Darsalena hurriedly followed after him. I followed behind them to the front door and I saw them get into a white Five Sixty SEL Mercedes Benz and they sped off. Just like that!

Darsalena said nothing more to me. I didn't get the chance to tell her I would be leaving tomorrow for Lagos to fly back to America. She was gone. I knew she had been desperately trying to come up with money to secure counsel for her brother-in-law who was in prison. And, I wondered whether my luncheon date with this millionaire had something to do with her efforts to get money.

Well, she wasn't going to use me if I could help it. I was paying for my own place to stay and I'm pulling out of here first thing Wednesday. I dismissed with thoughts about her just as she had dismissed with me.

I went over to the front desk and the guy that had been helping me was there. I asked him if he could

158

make some more arrangements for me. I needed a ride to the small airport tomorrow, so, I could fly to Lagos for my flight back to the good old U.S. He said that he would make some arrangements for me.

I went back to the front door to look for the man who cooked the meat outside, but, it was rainy and he was nowhere to be found. I hoped that the weather would change so he would come rescue me from the hunger I was now beginning to feel.

I went back up to my hotel room to just sit around and look out of the window and read. I felt sad. I was depending on that man outside to cook for me.   Didn't he sense how much I needed him to get food to eat? But, how could he? He probably thought I was having the time of my life here in Nigeria.   I wished Darsalena's uncle had come back to see me, but, I didn't see him again.

My phone rang and the guy at the front desk said there was a man here to see me. I said I would be right down, thinking it was Emmanuel who had come to be with me. He had come back from London. He had not forgotten me. In the elevator, I could feel my heart beating fast. I was very excited to see Emmanuel again.

So much for counting my chickens before they hatched! It wasn't him! It was one of his friends coming to give me a message from Emmanuel no doubt. I was wrong again!

Emmanuel's friend said he came to see how I was doing for his own knowledge. How did he know where to find me? I asked him, who directed him to this place? I didn't get his answer to this question because I started coughing all over the place. Emmanuel's friend said he had to leave and would see me later and left before I could say anything else to him.

The hotel clerk who had been so helpful to me and who still remains anonymous to me, even today, took me aside. He told me that Emmanuel and his friends had been making plans for me. I asked this guy to explain just what he meant that they were making plans for me.

His English was laden with such a heavy accent. He was speaking to me rapidly. I was not able to understand all of what he was saying. His words were not clear. He kept looking around as if he was worried about someone seeing him talking to me.

I was sick. I couldn't sleep last night because I felt so congested and everything. I was tired, I had the chills, and my head was hurting. I was achy all over and I didn't have a thing to eat or any medicine to take. I was now in the lobby just loitering.

Even though the casino was still open, I wouldn't dare go back there to be robbed again. I felt sorry for all the people who were in there. If I could, I would have broken into that slot machine and opened it to get my money out of it. Thief!

I was down to the last bit of my money. It was good for me that the U.S. dollar was worth five naira. It turned out that my hotel stay was only twenty-five U.S. dollars a night. I was using my credit card here and I was reaching my limit fast because of all the cash advances I had already made.

By the time I leave, I will have reached my maximum on my credit card. Many things and expenses in Nigeria required currency, cash only! I was just about to ask the hotel front desk clerk what he meant about Emmanuel and his friends. But then Emmanuel's friend walked back in the door.

I thought maybe I could get him to take me to a pharmacy. He was looking around. I know he was looking for me. This time, he said Emmanuel had told him to find me for him to see if I was all right.

He must have been joking earlier when he said he was looking for me for himself. He probably wanted to see how I would respond to that thought. He got no positive response from me. I believed Emmanuel wanted him to find me for him to see if I was okay. Or maybe

162

that's what I wanted to believe.

I started wondering if there was someone following me. Oh well, anyhow, Emmanuel's friend was here. He had shown up two days after I arrived at this hotel and I was very, very sick. My coughing had gotten much worse and I had no medicine to take to help me get some much needed sleep. Consequently, I asked Emmanuel's friend to take me to a drug store and to get something to eat. I told him I would pay him for the ride. He agreed to take me. And, when we got to his car, I was taken by the fact that he was driving a sparkling new three hundred series white, clean, and shiny Mercedes Benz. The seats were white leather, soft leather. He opened the door for me and as soon as he got in he flipped on his stereo system and it sounded wonderful. You could tell it was an expensive one.

He started the car and we stayed parked right outside of the hotel for awhile. I was wondering what he was waiting for. I frowned to myself thinking he looked very young to own this car. Then I thought of the chief's daughter and her wealth and dismissed the car as maybe a family inheritance of some sort.

We finally drove off. We drove for a ways; as usual, nothing close by here in Nigeria. And he played some good music he had on his cassette tapes. Songs I recognized from the States. I started thinking of Emmanuel and wishing this was his car and that he was here driving me around.

I didn't think much about Frank, my old boyfriend back in the United States. But then by late tonight, I had no idea that I would change my thoughts about Emmanuel. And that I would also feel stupid for getting in this car with this person calling himself Emmanuel's friend. But, I was ill, I needed medicine. I needed care.

We pulled up to this shack about five feet by five feet in size. He got out and I cautiously got out too.

164

Valerie Owens

I was scared about this place Emmanuel's friend had brought me to. It didn't look like a drug store to me.

There was some kind of business sign hanging over the door. It was in another language, and that's right, I couldn't read it. However, I was relieved to see a female, carrying a small child, come out of the door which was falling off its hinges.

I followed Emmanuel's friend inside. Sure enough, it was some kind of medicine place. It was dimly lit and there were uneven shelves around the back wall of the place. Nothing was in any kind of order and it looked like the man, behind the counter, had one of everything: bottles, pill containers, and boxes of things.

Emmanuel's friend began to talk to the man behind the counter and then he asked me what my sickness symptoms were. I described, to him, that I had a very harsh cough that hurt my chest badly each time I coughed and that my nose was stopped up. I said I was very congested and could not sleep.

Emmanuel's friend told the man what I had said. This man behind the counter was dressed in regular street clothes. I didn't know if he was a pharmacist or not. He had no white uniform on and he had no name/title tag on him. Shucks, I'll just call him the medicine man.

Well, then the medicine man moved down to the opposite end of the counter and pointed at a shelf in the corner. Emmanuel's friend told me he said to pick anything I wanted from that shelf. I thought anything? How should I know what I need? I'm not knowledgeable about medicines and drugs.

The medicine man gestured again with insistence that I pick. Accordingly, I picked a brown bottle hoping it was cough syrup. I paid the thirty-five naira and the medicine man gave the bottle to me. I put it into my pocketbook and we were off in Emmanuel's friend's lovely car

166

again. We were on the road for a long time again.

Next, we stopped to get some chicken and rice at an outdoor vendor. Cooking outside in Nigeria was common at the places I had been. This vendor had containers and bags for the food. I got one order since Emmanuel's friend said he wasn't hungry. He was on the thin side and didn't look like he ate at all. He said he needed to make a stop somewhere before he took me back to the hotel. So, I sat my bag of food on the floor in the back of his car and I prayed I wouldn't forget it.

We drove to this really nice house in the middle of nowhere. He drove through the gate that surrounded the property. Again, I thought why couldn't I have been visiting with someone who had all of this?

He got out of the car and again walked over to get the car door for me. I thanked him and we walked up to the door of this grand house. The door opened and a man ushered us in. I felt my inner alarm go off. We were directed to a plush living room area and seated.

With the grace of African kings, two men came in to greet us. They were handsome, beautiful, strong looking, clean, neat, good smelling men. Both were dressed in full African garb.

After they greeted me, the men began to speak in their native tongue and none of their words were understood by me. This was rude. This was crazy. I couldn't live like this. You just didn't know what people were saying, especially about you.

Then, I started thinking back about what the hotel desk clerk was trying to tell me. He started saying something about Emmanuel and his friends having plans for me and he looked very concerned. What was he trying to tell me? I kept looking at these men who were talking in another language and occasionally turning to look at me. I wanted to say to them, "What are you saying?

Does it somehow involve me?" But, how could it, I don't know these men.

With a sigh, Emmanuel's friend told me we would leave now. Some words were again exchanged between the men and we walked out to the car. I wanted to get back to the hotel. I wanted my refuge from this peculiar happening. I say it was peculiar because when we were leaving the men began to talk to me in perfect English. What was so secretive that they had to engage in conversation so that I could not understand it?

Forget them! Forget Emmanuel's friend! Forget this place! I asked Emmanuel's friend to take me back to the hotel. I said I wasn't feeling well and that I wanted to take my medicine. I said nothing more. I said nothing about my plans to leave Nigeria tomorrow.

When we got back to the hotel, he insisted on seeing me in. He walked right into the elevator and went straight up to my hotel room with me. I wasn't letting him come in. As I put my key into the door, he started being flirtatious. He was telling me, he was a better man than Emmanuel could ever have been. I thought oh no, Emmanuel told him we had been intimate and here he is trying to make his "play."

With the force of the "Exorcist" on my face, I told him good night. I meant it, good-bye, and good riddance. Then I thought to myself, "Nothing intimate was special between a man and woman, even in this country." I was angry. What kind of woman had Emmanuel made me out to be? Was this culture strict on following the Bible principle that only the married should have sex? And I was being viewed as loose and available to others because I was single?

I opened my door, Emmanuel's friend stepped forward and I had to push him in his chest back away from my door. I backed inside my hotel room and I slammed the door shut.

I started crying. My feelings were hurt. My reputation may be

170

tainted. I completely forgot that crying and colds and congestion don't go together. I made myself feel worse. The little ability I had to breathe through my nose was completely gone. I could only breathe through my mouth.

I got ready for bed. I pulled out the medicine I had purchased. On closer inspection of the bottle, it turned out to be labeled with somebody's name and prescription information on it. Plus, its expiration date had expired a year ago. What was this? Did someone steal a person's prescription and like a pawn shop item turn it in to this medicine man for money?

Or did the medicine man go around stealing medicine from people to stock his shelves and then resell it? Or did he find the medicines thrown out in the trash and retrieved them to sell? Or were these prescriptions filled, unclaimed, and then they ended up sold or given to the medicine man to sell to someone else, namely me? Gee whiz! I didn't know what to say or think about this place.

My phone rang. Who is it now? Not another disappointment... please. It was the helpful hotel desk clerk. It was now the ungodly hour of two a.m. I suppose he's calling now because surely there wasn't anybody in the lobby that could overhear his conversation with me. Then he could take his time and explain what he was trying to tell me earlier today. He said that I must hurry and pack now. That he has arranged for my ride to start my journey to the Lagos International Airport for about six a.m.

I said "Six a.m.! That's too early." He continued to talk explaining why I needed to leave so early. And I had only to believe him or be wrong and suffer the consequences. He said that Emmanuel was now associated with two wealthy Nigerian women who derived their wealth partly from manufacturing cloth for African garb fabric and partly from selling and/or

172

pimping women. He said that I would come at a high price to some rich Nigerian man since I was not only educated, but, I had attractive looks.

I couldn't believe what I was hearing. I sat silently thinking back over the events that had happened to me. I sat thinking about the two rich looking Nigerian women in the apartment asking me all those questions and the two rich Nigerian men Emmanuel's friend introduced me to.

I thought about all of them talking in front of me in their "native tongue" when they knew English perfectly. I thought of the money that must have paid for all those drugs in that apartment. I thought about the ease at which Darsalena let Emmanuel know where I was and how to find me. And the ease at which she let him take me when he had found me at the wedding reception.

I thought about the money Darsalena desperately needed for her brother-in-law in prison and the millionaire she brought to take me to lunch. I remembered his attitude when I refused to go. I remembered the uncle's anger at Darsalena and the fact that I had not reached the university where I was supposed to be going all along. There wasn't even any more talk about working on the research Darsalena had asked me to come to Nigeria to help do. No mention of her dissertation. Now, I wondered, what was the real purpose of my being on this trip?

The hotel clerk urged me to go, get out now! He and Darsalena's uncle were the only ones who seemed to have cared anything about me so far.

I got up and hurriedly packed all my things. I just could not believe that I didn't bring one pair of pants on this trip. Can you believe it? All I had were dresses and skirts and not even a denim skirt. I needed something more roughed to wear for my long journey ahead.

With all my things locked away,

I called the hotel clerk and told him my things were ready and I needed a little sleep. I was now feeling groggy from the medicine I had taken before he called to warn me about my association with Emmanuel. He said he would call me in three hours; a wake-up call.

Just as fast as I'm writing this line, it seemed the time went by. My phone was ringing and I could hear it but I didn't want to wake up. I wanted to stay in bed under my six or seven blankets and sleep. Sleep! Sleep! Sleep!

But, I couldn't quite ignore the noise of the ringing. I reached over and answered it. It was the hotel clerk telling me it was time to get up and prepare myself to leave, now, while I could. I thanked him for waking me.

At first, after I had hung up the phone, I just laid there on the bed trying to collect myself. I know I had been dreaming, but about what I couldn't remember. I kept trying to make myself remember. I could sense that it was a very involved dream, in REM sleep no doubt.

Like a flash of light, I started remembering parts of my dream. It involved the little girl who had been buried, the two young boys stoned to death, my sickness and something chasing me. In the dream, I was running scared. I don't know what was chasing me?

When I went into the bathroom and turned on the light, I was shocked at the way my hair looked. My mother had pressed my hair with a hot comb in wax so that it would stay straightened for this trip. Though the days were hot, they were not humid. My hair had stayed pressed straight and smooth for twenty-eight days.

For about three hours, I had slept and either the dream I had, or a fever I didn't know I had, did a job on my hair. I didn't have a hat, a wig or scarf to cover it with. I didn't even have time to wet it and apply lotion to it and let it dry pulled back tight. As if I didn't look bad enough.

Valerie Owens

There's nothing like a bad hairdo day that can bring you down emotionally.

I tried to pull my hair back as best as I could with no success at getting various humps and bumps out of it. I thought please don't let anyone I know run into me on the way back to the States. I suppose there's no sense in hemming and hawing right now. I can certainly fix myself back up later on.

I quickly got dressed and called down to the front desk for help to get my luggage down to the hotel lobby. Just as soon as I came down, my driver had arrived. It was not the driver I had before, but, there was no time to quibble over that. I was leaving here today. I thanked the guy behind the front desk over and over for caring about me and I said goodbye.

The cab driver and I went out the front door and, golly wow, there sat his cab that would be my chariot out of there, if it made it the distance. It had three doors and no seat in the back. I had to sit on the springs. The

windows didn't open up. This part of my travels would take well over three hours. The cabby had been paid up front to drive me and I hoped there would be no quirks involved in this ride. No flat tire, no running out of gas, etcetera, etcetera.

There was barely any light in the sky when we left that morning. Sitting, in the taxi, alone with this stranger, who couldn't even speak English, made me start thinking hard. I thought about the seven feet high bushes that were close on both sides of the road we were traveling. I thought about how do I know that this strange man will drive me to the airport? I had paid him the last of the money I had except for three dollars.

I began planning in my mind what I would do if this man attacks me. I read somewhere that you can use your keys as a weapon. And really that's all I had useful in my purse; the keys to my apartment, my mother's house and my aunt's house. I took them out and I told

Valerie Owens

**myself if I have to defend myself, I
must do so by striking where it would
hurt most, his eyes, his nose or his
testicles.** Whichever place my hand
ended up in, I must be prepared to
strike hard.** But, then I thought,
that's only if there was some kind of
struggle.** If he turns around and just
shoots me in the head, I'm a sure
goner then.**

**With every move he made, I
jumped.** I hoped he hadn't noticed,
but I couldn't help it.** I was afraid.
Not one thing had gone as planned on
this trip and my anxiety level was
very high.** I wanted to end this whole
nightmare today.**

**I kept alert even though it was
a struggle to keep from falling back
fast asleep.** There was nothing to
look at on either side of the road
except tall grass bushes.** Where was
the road I had traveled on when I
came to this place?** I didn't even
know if this strange man was even
taking me where I needed to go.**

**I started praying for safety as I
had not ever prayed before.** Please**

179

let me stay alive until I get back to my mother to tell her all about what had happened to me here.

He kept looking through his rear view mirror. I didn't like that. I tried to look hard, like I would be something to tangle with, this being short of him having a gun. I thought of retaliation if this man so much as coughed, too, close to me. I was thinking big thoughts. Please don't let me have to put actions behind them.

The sun began to get brighter and the warm sun rays on my face began to relax the frown that had become a part of my countenance since we began this ride. Surely, the cabby could figure by now I wasn't about to fall asleep and I was watching his every move. Like I knew where we were going!

Maybe he didn't know this was my first trip and that I didn't know where I was going. I didn't give a hoot about what he thought about me; he just better not try anything. All the anger I had built up since being on this trip would be aimed at him.

Thank you. We're here! The cab driver simply took out my luggage and placed it at the front door of this small airport and drove off without a word. The luggage porter took my luggage in and I counted out a dollar in U.S. coins and gave it to him.

My ticket was checked and within the hour I was flying back to Lagos, to the Nigerian International Airport, on a small plane that sat maybe forty people. The flight there was short, about two hours.

I arrived at the Lagos airport about eleven a.m. I would have to sit with my two large pieces of luggage and my purse for eleven hours. The flight to the U.S. didn't leave until a little after ten p.m. I was there to catch my flight and that's all that mattered now. I didn't care about anything else, at least for that moment. Fortunately, where I sat I could see the ticket counter and U.S. flight number.

America Huh! I'm Going Home

Valerie Owens

Chapter 4: On My Own
♦♦♦♦♦♦♦

America Huh! I'm Going Home

Valerie Owens

I began to look through a magazine that someone had left in the seat next to mine. I had grown tired of the algebra book I was working problems in and I had finished the book "Fear of Flying" I had been reading. It was really a good book. I didn't want to put it down. I just wanted to read more and more.

The airport was very crowded. People were constantly walking pass me. Black people! I knew there had to be some other ethnic groups around, somewhere. However, I saw none there. All of the employees were Black. All of the vendors were Black.

Speaking of vendors, you could smell the food items: coffee, hot dogs, and popcorn. I was so hungry

185

and thirsty. But, it was a good thing that I hadn't drank or eaten anything. It would have been impossible for me to go to the ladies room carrying, all of my, luggage. If I got one there, my other luggage would have been left unattended to and probably stolen.

I didn't see anyone that I felt I could trust to watch my things. So I just held in my urine and hoped that I didn't get a bladder infection which I so often got from holding so long. Yet, again, this couldn't be helped.

The time went by oh so slowly. I started to think back to what that hotel clerk had told me about Emmanuel and his friends. It made me sad, angry, and disappointed and scared at how people can have little regard for your life, your happiness, and your desires. They only sought their own desires no matter how they negatively affected another. I didn't want any of this to be true, especially, about Emmanuel. I liked him. I wanted to be with him again.

Then I thought of Frank. What

186

about Frank? He was just Frank. There was nothing exciting about him at all. In fact, he was somewhat of a bore. He had no aspirations, dreams, or desires beyond being a lover man.

I wondered how much this trip had changed me. It certainly opened my eyes up to a whole different way of living and made me start appreciating my own life more.

I kept looking at my watch. Tick, tick, tick, slowly the time went by. My stomach started growling. I couldn't buy anything to eat. I needed my last two U.S. dollars to tip the luggage porters back in America. There would be one porter in New York and one porter in Philadelphia. The tip should have been more, but, that's all I had. It was better than nothing at all.

It was dark out now and in just a little while longer the flight would be boarding. I didn't dare fall asleep here for fear when I awakened I would have had my luggage stolen and missed my flight; after all, who would wake me in time.

My eyes were tired; they were burning. I started thinking about Jesus when he asked the disciples to stay awake and on watch while he was on the Mount of Olives in the garden of Gethsemane praying. I should have been there, I'm marathon material. But, when I did sleep, eventually, again, I promised myself I was going to sleep until my heart's content.

With my suitcases, I decided to wait my last hour for the flight in the boarding line. I dragged each suitcase over, one at a time. I wanted to be first to board. Quickly, the line began to form after I stood up. Copycats! The line was long! Many people were getting on this flight.

The ticket agent finally arrived. He began to fiddle with things behind the counter and then made his announcements to the passengers who were to board the flight to the United States. He said to me, "May I have your tickets and passport." I eagerly gave them to him and he looked at them and then told me to step aside.

He said that my flight was not until next Wednesday, a week from today. I told him that I paid a travel agent in Port Harcourt to have my flight changed. He said he had no such change and demanded that I step aside. I couldn't argue my point because he began speaking to the next person who had been behind me.

I moved my luggage close to where I had been sitting. I had this heavy feeling in my heart. My stomach felt queasy. I had no more money. I would have to live in this airport for a week because I wasn't leaving here until I could go back to the States. I thought I probably will get locked up for loitering.

How could this happen? Why did the lady take my money and not do what I paid her to do? Why me? Did Emmanuel have something to do with this?

Just then, I looked up and coming toward me was Emmanuel

and one of those wealthy looking Nigerian women I met at that apartment. Emmanuel came to me like we were distant friends. His warmth was restrained, maybe gone. I don't know.

The lady did all the talking. She said she wanted me to come with her. She said that I had not really seen Nigeria, and that I had not been shown a good time here. That was an understatement.

She said she wanted me to come with them and stay with her. I told her I was all out of money and I wanted to go back to the States to get money. I told her I was an only child and that I was worried about my mother. I told her anything I could think of.

She asked me if I would come back to Nigeria and knowing I wouldn't look in this direction again, if only I could now get back to America, I said, "I promise, I'll come back again."

Emmanuel asked for my forwarding address and telephone

190

Valerie Owens

number. I knew I probably shouldn't
have given him the correct numbers.
But, I did think somehow that once
back on familiar territory I would be
able to shield myself from anything
bad that these individuals could do to
me.

Therefore, I quickly jotted the
information down on the piece of
paper Emmanuel had given to me and
gave him it and his pen back. Boy
was he distant.

I told them what had happened
to me with my ticket and like a
parrot, I kept repeating I wanted to
go back home, I wanted to go back
home, I wanted to go back home.

The lady told me to wait where I
was. Emmanuel started to talk to me
about how he had missed me while
the lady went over and talked to the
ticket agent. I wondered why
Emmanuel had not said he missed me
when that lady had been present. I
wished good things for us. Like a
character in a romantic novel, I
wanted him to fall in love with me
and me with him. I wanted us to

make plans together. **Maybe he could teach me how to speak Nigerian.**

The next thing I knew the lady told me to follow her saying that she had gotten me aboard in VIP seating. Emmanuel checked in my luggage and they walked me to the VIP room and left. Just like that. Boy, no goodbyes, no safe flight wishes, no kisses or hugs. They were just gone.

I sat down with the few others who had VIP seating. Then I thought about what the lady with Emmanuel had told me. She said she had told the ticket agent that I was her friend from the U.S. and that I wanted to go on this flight. The VIP seating instantly became mine. I thanked her, but, as I recollect, she didn't appear happy with my decision to go. She seemed annoyed even, just like those two Nigerian men and that Nigerian millionaire.

But, that was all behind me now. They were gone. Yet, I felt my heart hurting over Emmanuel's departure and his lack of attention. Who was this woman to him that he would change his disposition so abruptly? Or was this the case of "Slam bam thank you Mam?" Or was he just cold acting?

Forget him, I thought and knowing in my heart, it wasn't going to be that easy. Why is it so hard to let go when you like someone? Is it the dreams you have about the person? Is it your stubbornness that won't let you let go? Is it because you want to go through the pain of letting what is not good for you be a controlling factor in your life? What was it?

They started boarding the VIP passengers. On I went and took my seat. I was right in front of the partition used to show movies. It was the left seat in the middle two rows. The airplane doors were closed and the airplane began taxiing away.

All of a sudden, the plane jerked to a sudden stop. My heart began to beat fast, faster, and faster. The airplane doors were reopened and police came onto the plane.

I began saying please to myself,

so much, that I could have dropped down on one knee and did James Brown's record. "Please! Please! Please!" Please, don't let them come for me.

Two police went down each aisle. I was scared out of my mind. I felt my heart would beat right out of my chest. I kept thinking, "Please, please, please, please, please, don't let them take me off this flight."

I didn't pay for VIP seating. I just wanted to be on this flight! And then I could hear some screams in the back of the plane. The police dragged this Nigerian man off of the plane and a woman with a child was hollering and crying out to him.

The airplane doors shut again and we began taxiing away. I thought please let us get out of here this time. I felt the aircraft begin to ascend into the air. My heart calmed down and I began to breathe normally again.

I remembered that earlier, I was panting like I was about to have an asthma attack when I don't even suffer from asthma. I thought I would faint and need to be resuscitated.

The flight attendant began to give the passengers the instructions on what to do in the case of an emergency. I tried to release my grip of the arms of my seat. I'm sure I would have carried that seat with me if they had tried to take me off this plane. I was surprised I hadn't broken, all, or any, of my fingernails from holding so tight.

I started counting trying to relax. I felt a bad headache coming on. It might have come from not eating anything for such a long while. I wished they'd give me the food/snack they would be serving. I needed some nourishment.

However, first the flight attendants passed around headphones for the movie they were about to show. Movie, I hope it's a good one. I hope it is one that could help take my mind off of things for a little while. I need a "mental activity" break.

Yea! Eddie Murphy's movie, "Beverly Hills Cop." Lights out and now I can really get into this movie. Besides I needed the laugh.

Gee, he's such a handsome brown man. His neckline was so clean. His hair cut was razor sharp neat. Boy, why couldn't I meet a man like that, I thought to myself?

No, instead I meet men with nothing going for them. No dreams and no dreams fulfilled. Frank worked for the U.S. Postal Service. I suppose I couldn't talk. I worked for them too. But, I'm trying to do better, much better. And Emmanuel, I don't know what his game was. I always wanted a strong, achieving, goal oriented, positive man in my life. I've not had the pleasure.

I enjoyed the movie and now with a little food in my stomach, I was ready for some shut eye. I needed a blanket or two since they always kept airplanes so cold. Sleep will be so good right now. Hmm!

Eventually, I awakened to the flight attendant asking if I wanted something else to drink. I asked for some hot tea, with lemon and extra sugar.

I looked around and it seemed like I was the only one awake now. I wondered why, of all the passengers – why did the flight attendant, end up bothering me? I needed sleep probably more than anyone else on the plane. Then, I was thinking maybe I was talking in my sleep and she thought I was awake, crazy maybe, but awake.

It was enjoyable to feel the soothing effect of drinking down the hot tea. I needed every relaxing thing and comfort anyone could bring. This trip and all of what I had endured hadn't sunk in yet.

Nor, had I come to grips with the fact that I was on my way back to the States. I may have been experiencing cultural shock. I felt numb, empty, stripped of my self esteem, broken, worn out, and weather-beaten.

I went to the airplane restroom and took a good look at myself in the mirror. I didn't look at all like me. The person sitting next to me said little to me. How could I blame him? I probably looked pretty shady.

Twelve hours on this flight seemed so long. It seemed like we wouldn't ever land. I tried to fall back asleep, but I couldn't. Maybe the caffeine from the hot tea stimulated me. I wanted to talk. I wanted to tell someone all about what had just happened to me, but there was no one friendly towards me.

I started making plans in my mind of the things I would do just as soon as I got to Philly. I sure as heck was going to make an appointment to get a facial, body wax, electrolysis treatment, pedicure, and manicure. I was going to wash my hair and get my mother to press it straight again. I was going to go out and eat at the finest restaurant. I couldn't wait! Hurry -- get me to the States again!

I began to think of Emmanuel again. I wondered where he was and whether or not I'd ever see him

again. Why was I drawn to this man so? I just couldn't figure it out or explain it. Still, I wanted there to be more between us than "two ships passing in the night."

Only, when I really thought about things, I really didn't know much about him. Was he single or married, a father or not, his age, his address, phone number, occupation, last name? All I knew was I was very attracted to him in the strangest way.

America Huh! I'm Going Home

Valerie Owens

Chapter 5: There Is No Place Like Home
◆◆◆◆◆◆◆

America Huh! I'm Going Home

I heard the pilot announce our arrival to the United States. **WE ARE HERE!** Thank Jehovah God. I'm in America again. I could taste the tears running down my face. I didn't care what people thought. **WE WERE HERE!** I wanted to get down on my knees and kiss the ground I walked on. I was so happy to be back there. New York!

I had only a little time to get to the terminal to take a shuttle plane from New York to Philadelphia. I rushed in with the crowd to a shuttle bus that transported me to the correct terminal. When I got out of the shuttle bus, my eyes landed upon the face of the most gorgeous White, blond-haired, and blue-eyed man I have ever seen. He looked so refined, so rich.

He had gotten out of a stretch black limousine. I stared at him hard forgetting myself for a minute. I became mesmerized by the number of Louis Vuitton luggage he had. The porters were carting it inside on about seven luggage carts. He had at least fifty pieces. It all was looking brand new. This man had to be rich and famous. I went into the small terminal behind him looking like the latest thing from the homeless. There was a crowd to the left side of me, but I ignored it since all I could see was the ticket agent that could get me to my Philadelphia destiny.

And right outside the terminal door, I could see the small plane that could fly me there. When I approached the ticket agent, she told me to take a seat. She said it would be awhile before the next shuttle plane could transport me. She said that Eddie Murphy was filming a movie in here right now.

I didn't hear her -- believe me. All I could see was the shuttle plane just beyond the door to the right side

204

Valerie Owens

of me and I wanted to leave on it. I insisted that I be put on that plane.

I know I had to look crazy. My hair was nappy, my makeup smeared, but, mostly wiped off, my clothes were wrinkled. I kept saying I wanted to get on that plane.

She said wait, she would call the shuttle plane to see if they would seat me. And the next thing I knew, she was directing me to the door to the shuttle plane. I boarded and sat in my seat and moments later, the shuttle plane took off.

Then the worse feeling came over me. Did she say Eddie Murphy was filming a movie in that terminal where they were going to let me sit? Were the movie people setting up things? I felt sick. This was the man I had wished to meet and he wasn't even married then.

Someone on board said he was shooting the movie "Coming To America." It was a story about an African prince traveling to America. I just came from Africa. I could have given him a real story to tell. I wanted to go back! But, it was too late.

I could have tried to get discovered as an extra, something. I could have knocked something over, lighting, maybe, and gotten noticed. Oh, I was sick. I didn't think I could feel any worse.

I kept trying to convince myself that I looked too awful to have approached or attempted to approach such a "clean-cut" man such as Eddie Murphy. But, the sick feeling would not leave. Somehow I felt I had messed up a golden opportunity that would not ever come again. And it hasn't.

Back in Philly, I had one dollar left to tip the luggage porter. I caught a cab from the Philadelphia International Airport. Once we were three quarters of the way to my apartment in Conshohocken, I told the driver to stop at an ATM automatic teller machine; he did. Knowing this cab ride was really going to cost me, I withdrew seventy dollars. I didn't call my mother to come for me because I wanted to go to my apartment and try to get my head clear. The cab ride cost me fifty dollars even; so I tipped the driver for carrying my luggage in.

I opened my apartment door and it looked so beautiful within. My white baby grand piano was all shiny and clean. My dusty, rose, colored couch was all soft and neat. My black lacquer Japanese chair was glossy and smooth. The view out my sliding glass door window that overlooked a lake was beautiful. Magnificent! One really doesn't appreciate what one has until one doesn't have it for awhile.

The first thing I did was go to the refrigerator. I opened the freezer and stuck my head in. I wanted to feel the cool frost blowing over my head. After a few moments, I quickly went into my bathroom and stripped off all my clothing. I wanted to burn them. Then I thought that would be losing my head.

Stepping into my shower, I proceeded to lather up with my

favorite shower gel, the Niki de Saint Phalle fragrance. Why did they have to discontinue this fragrance in America? I love it!

I don't know how long the thousand dollars worth of perfume, lotion, soap, cologne, and powder, I purchased will last me. But, it wouldn't last forever. I'm glad the store representative alerted me to the discontinuation of my most desired fragrance. There was some falling out between the Paris perfume company and the distributors here in the United States.

Ah, that feels so good! I let the warm water just run down my body. I closed my eyes. I didn't want to move. It felt so good to be in my shower -- a real shower with real soap.

After rinsing off, I reluctantly turned the water off. My soft, fluffy, and clean towel awaited me. But, more than that, my Victoria's Secret lingerie was lined up in my closet. What shall I wear? I felt like fuchsia. So fuchsia it shall be with black

208

feathered and satin slippers.

Oh! This was such a wonderful feeling. America huh! Home! This was my home, all that I grew up with, and all that I knew.

I decided to call my mother and to my alarm she began crying over me and asked me to please come to be with her. Since it was now apparent that my trip didn't just affect me negatively, I couldn't refuse my mother's wish.

Putting on my black stretch jeans, a blouse, a hat, and some make-up, I drove back to Philly. My car started right up even though it had been sitting for twenty nine days. Go red Camaro baby! I was glad I didn't get caught in any traffic jams. I couldn't stomach the tension and chaos.

As soon as my mother opened the door, she kissed me and hugged me. The next thing she was fixing me something to eat. She told me to eat and then go wash my hair. She probably knew under my hat my hair was looking very tacky.

I was really tired, so I asked my mother if I could wash my hair, stay the night, and get my hair done maybe in the morning or afternoon or evening or whenever I woke up naturally. She agreed.

I didn't bother calling Frank. I couldn't just yet. I was still fighting with stronger feelings I had for Emmanuel. I didn't want to deal with Frank now. I didn't want him to bother me. Not now.

When I finally woke up the next day, it was almost evening. My mother had left my favorite fried Whiting fish, mashed potatoes and the corn I loved. I know it was two starches, but when you are starving, it all benefits you the same. She left me a note telling me she had gone to do some hair, signed Mommy.

I decided to watch television. Something I rarely did. However, the television was there and it had more than one channel on which a show could appear.

I'd say after about two hours I heard my Mother opening the front door. I went to her and helped her carry her bags in and kissed her good day. She had stopped at the food market and bought me my favorite ice cream, Breyers butter almond. It's great how mothers know just what their children like and make the effort to please them with those things. Too bad many men don't exercise that gesture; it would make happier women in their lives.

My mother wanted to rest a bit before she did my hair. We watched some television together. She likes game shows. I like love stories or movies. But, I watched attentively what she wanted to watch anyway.

The next thing I knew, she was laid out on her couch asleep, snoring even. I knew she was probably tired, so I resolved to stay another night at my mother's house.

I had no pressing place to go. My salon appointments weren't until Saturday and I could certainly leave from here to go there. And I was still on sick leave from my postal job due to a car accident requiring surgery and physical therapy. Yes, thanks to my paying for the loss wages option within my Allstate car insurance policy, I was living a "Life of Raleigh" until my trip to Nigeria.

I started thinking about Emmanuel again. I wondered where he was and whether or not he would think of me again. I couldn't get this man off my mind. I didn't even want to see Frank. Here in the States, I wanted to see Emmanuel again.

Wouldn't you know that I saw Emmanuel in my dreams this same night and I didn't want my dream to end, but it did? My dream ended when I heard my mother calling me, in the morning, to come downstairs to get my hair done.

Nothing like the smell of washed and pressed Black hair smoking up the kitchen. I always wanted to eat my breakfast first. But, invariably, my mother had to do my hair first because she at all times had somewhere to go.

All the hair my mother has done for free, since she was twenty years

Valerie Owens

old, I declare, she should have had a shop, a nice little nest egg, and a fabulous home by now. No, however, this wasn't the case. Just think where all that potential money could have gone.

Now with my hair done, I said my goodbye to my mother and off to the salon I went to get my facial, body wax, manicure, and pedicure. By seven p.m., I was groomed from head to toe. What a wonderful feeling to be all "aglow." Feeling like I was worth a million dollars, I went back to my apartment and I was lying around watching television and my telephone.

Literally, for the next three days, I was waiting for my telephone to ring. And then my phone rang. I jumped up to answer it on a half of a ring hoping, praying it was Emmanuel.

It was Frank. How did he know I was home? Everything he had to say to me was unkind. He was angry that I had been home for a week and hadn't phoned. He had seen me

213

driving by in my car; otherwise, he would have thought I was still gone.

I wished I was. I didn't need Frank's hassling of me. I'm trying to sort out my feelings about a man who I couldn't stop thinking or dreaming of. I wanted Emmanuel to want me for himself as much as I wanted him. I didn't want to believe that Emmanuel wanted to sell me.

I wasn't even paying attention to Frank and all of what he had to say because my heart was hurting for the man I had to leave behind. Frank hung up the telephone on me and then I hung up too.

Once thoroughly settled back in my apartment in Conshohocken, Pennsylvania, part of me just did not want to totally believe that Emmanuel could be involved in any plots to use me to gain money. I wanted to love this man, but I knew I couldn't continue to feel this way if he was guilty of wanting to do something like that to me.

Days later, I received my first call from Emmanuel. I wanted to be

214

happy and excited. However, I thought should I be? I loved his voice, his accent, the way he talked to me and the things he said. Please let the hotel clerk guy be wrong about Emmanuel. Let Emmanuel just have stumbled onto the wrong kinds of friends.

Then Emmanuel asked me to come to El Paso, Texas to visit with him at his home. I was ready to see him. I was stronger now. I was on familiar ground. I couldn't invite him to come see me with Frank lurking around. I needed more time to make up my mind though my heart was made up already.

Emmanuel purchased my round trip ticket for just a little more than a weekend stay since he said he had to work and was attending school full-time.

On Thursday afternoon, I arrived at the airport and Emmanuel was at the airport on time to pick me up. I was so glad he wasn't late. He took me in his arms and kissed me passionately. He was nothing like he was when I left Lagos, Nigeria. Why, I started thinking? The woman he was with could not have been anyone to him since she was there the first night he slept with me. Strange, I thought. However, now just let me enjoy this reunion with him.

He carried my one small suitcase to his car. Ah! Another white fancy car! It was a brand new BMW. Interesting I thought. Things got even better at least for a bit. He lived in a nice apartment building. And when he opened his apartment door I was left breathless. His place was immaculate, neat, and clean. Every item in there was modern and new looking. Everything was color coordinated.

He went to put on some music and for the first time I saw a six disc player. Big screen color television. Beautiful! Next he took me into his bedroom to place my luggage and things. I stepped into his walk-in closet. He had one complete row of suits; silk and tailored. He had one row of tailored-made shirts. He had

216

shoes neatly positioned side by side. He had ties galore. So very impressive! I L-O-V-E a well dressed man!

I asked to use his bathroom and once there, I saw that he had rows of cologne. The bathroom was spick-and-span clean. It was just like I love a place in which to live. My place was just like his.

Frank on the other hand, lived in a small room at his mother's and had none of these things, clothes or otherwise. Emmanuel, what a man, what a man!

We started talking and I finally got the nerve up to ask him if he had a girlfriend since there were no signs of a wife anywhere in his place. This was a bachelor's pad, but it was not your typical bachelor's pad...this place was fine! I was thoroughly taken by all this. Emmanuel said he had been dating Janet Jackson, but she was no longer seeing him. How could I compete with a woman like that? If she was anything like me, everything that he owned was from her money.

That thought didn't rub me right at all. Was Emmanuel some kind of gigolo? There I go trying to get into his head again. Why do I keep trying to know the story about this man? If I can just be patient, everything will come to light. It always does.

There was a knock on his door. It was one of his Nigerian friends. Emmanuel let him in. He introduced me as his lady. When did I become that, I wondered? He didn't say anything to me about that. When was my acceptance of this title? His friend took a seat. And I was thinking, why was this other man here?

Emmanuel said he was going to cook our dinner; he called it stew and fu fu (mashed yam balls). It was stew with balls that tasted like uncooked dough that you broke apart with your fingers and soaked up the stew juice with. It was so good! Emmanuel said he didn't make it as spicy as he normally did because he remembered I had a sensitive

218

stomach. How thoughtful of him.

Now his friend had eaten. When was he going to leave? Or, did he live here also? But, there was only one bedroom. I guess he could sleep on the sofa. Maybe the sofa was a hideaway bed.

Emmanuel's friend began to talk to Emmanuel in Nigerian. Now why was he doing that since up until now he had been speaking plain English? What is it with these people? Didn't they know that was rude? I sure didn't like it.

While they talked, I started looking in one of Emmanuel's magazines. Without thinking about it, I glanced at the mailing label. It had on it Emmanuel's first name, however, the last name was not the same name that I remembered Emmanuel giving me. I picked up four more magazines, pretending to look in them first. The other four had Emmanuel's first name but four different last names; five different last names in all. Not a good sign.

Emmanuel's friend finally found

it in his heart to get up and leave. I didn't say anything to Emmanuel about the mailing labels. I had to have a ride back to the airport when it was time for me to leave and I didn't want to rock the boat over some mail items.

Yet, I kept thinking about those five different last names. Which one was his real last name? Were any of them his real last name? Will the real Emmanuel _____ please stand up?

All of a sudden, the lights went out. I mean everything electric went off. I was thinking that all these modern devices and appliances he had, had blew a fuse. Then he informed me that the electric service had been cut off and that he didn't know why, since he had paid the bill. He said we would go see about it first thing in the morning.

It was dark outside and our choices for the night were to sit up in complete darkness or go get in the bed. Sure, we went and got into bed. We rolled in the sheets all night long. With that kind of activity, the lights being out went unnoticed.

I awakened to the sunlight shining in the window and my movement woke Emmanuel. We got up, dressed and on this Friday morning we were off to the electric company. When we got to the electric company, Emmanuel argued with the people about some check he had sent for his payment that the representative said they hadn't received yet.

With great disgust, Emmanuel walked away from the lady. I asked Emmanuel, what did the representative have to say? He said she said that in order to get his service back on today, he would have to pay for his bill today and deal with the lost check he said he sent if they ever received it. Then he told me that he had used up his money on my flight ticket and wouldn't have any money until he got paid again.

What else could I do but pay the electric bill? Call me crazy, but I wasn't about to sit in his apartment for three days without lights.

Besides, he said he would send me my money back when he got paid. He did pay for my plane ticket.

We left the electric company and almost adjacent to it was this restaurant. Emmanuel entered into it and took a seat. I'm thinking, "I hope you have the money for this food." I should have asked. He ordered and I ordered. Yes, and after we finished eating, he handed the bill to me. He was a gigolo! I paid it and we left.

Next, he stopped at his post office box and he removed a pile of mail from it. We went back to his place and I actually felt robbed. I tried to reason things out. He paid for my plane ticket round trip. He fed me mostly with his own food at home. Maybe he was a little low on funds this weekend, but, he still wanted me to be with him.

He had laid his mail down on his coffee table and when he went into the bathroom, I looked at his names on the envelopes. Again there were these different last names which

222

appeared with his first name Emmanuel. What was this man doing?

Emmanuel emerged from his bathroom and caught me looking through his pile of mail. So, I blatantly asked why he had so many different last names. He told me that he orders things like all the things he owns from places under an assumed name. He said that when he got the stuff he didn't pay for any of it.

He went on to show me how I could do this. I'm thinking about how all my property was bought from the sweat of my labor and here this man was getting his things free. And he was getting away with it.

I guess there were some advantages to having a whole other country to flee to when things got "hot" for you in the States. I didn't like Emmanuel for this. It made me feel uncomfortable with him. Like back in Nigeria when I was afraid, the police would raid that apartment with the drugs they had around me. Let the weekend hurry and end before this man has me in prison with him.

I was disenchanted with Emmanuel. It's a big turn off for me when a man lacks integrity. I went through the motions of being with him, though my thoughts had shifted back to Frank, hoping it was not too late to go back with him. I thought, "I'll put the Emmanuel experience behind me."

On my return to my apartment, I called Frank. I told him I wanted to date him again. Then Emmanuel kept calling and trying to talk to me but my feelings had changed for him.

However, one night, out of curiosity, I called Emmanuel's friend I met in Nigeria. Back in Nigeria Emmanuel's friend had secretly slipped me his Kansas City telephone number. He was pleasant so I talked with him a bit before I asked him things about Emmanuel.

He said Emmanuel was there in Kansas City. He said he lived there with his wife.

"Wife," I said, "You've got to be

224

joking."

He said, "No, I'm not kidding around. They will be right back." He said they went to get a bite to eat.

I felt like crying, dying. My emotions were all chaotic inside. We talked just a little bit longer and then Emmanuel's friend began talking to a male's voice.

He said, "Here Emmanuel, the phone is for you."

Emmanuel got on the line not knowing that I was on the other end. It was true. He was there.

Still, there was another voice, a female's voice calling for Emmanuel. I asked him, who was that? He said to give him ten minutes and he would call me back to explain. I told him he's got just ten minutes and that's it.

He called me back in eight minutes because I was watching the clock and counting the minutes.

He said that he was in fact married, but, in name only. He said he needed a green card so that he could stay in the United States and that he had paid this lady to marry him. I didn't know what to believe.

I asked him where was my money since he had money to fly to Kansas City. He said that he hadn't flown but drove to Kansas City and hadn't gotten paid yet. He asked me to please believe him that the marriage was one of convenience only.

He said that he loved me. How does a man prove his love? Better yet, how does a Black man prove his love to a Black woman?

He kept saying the same things over and over. He told me to be patient and that he would be free so that we could be together. I could feel myself wanting to believe him. With all the writing on the wall, I still wanted this man to be good. I wanted him for me. Dumb I was. Dumbfounded!

Day after day, Emmanuel kept calling me saying all the sweet kinds of things every woman likes to hear from a man. I was under his spell.

One day, he called me and

Valerie Owens

asked me if I loved him. I felt that I
did, so I said yes. Then he said if I
really loved him, I would steal blank
money orders from the United States
Postal Service. This man was mad!

First, I didn't even work with
blank money orders. Second, he was
asking me to commit a felony. In
essence, he was asking me to go to
prison. That's the love he had for me.
I told him to jump off the nearest
roof and I hung up the phone.

When the phone rang again, I
ignored its ring because I was crying
my eyes out over this man. I started
screening my calls. And when a great
opportunity arose for me to move
into a brand new town house for one-
hundred more dollars than I was
paying in rent for my apartment, I
moved. My telephone number was
changed and unlisted.

Six months later, I married
Frank trying to convince myself that
Frank was not a rebound. The first
telephone call I received on my
unlisted telephone number, after
returning from my honeymoon, was

227

from Emmanuel. He was telling me he was sorry and how much he loved me and please, give, him another chance. But, that's another story.

Valerie Owens

ACKNOWLEDGMENTS

In Pennsylvania –
I especially want to thank my mother, Eve-Lyn Williams, for living through my taking this trip against her wishes and my disappearance that caused her dreadful worry for twenty-eight days.

Thank you goes to my aunt, Sadie and cousins, Thomas, Linda, and Selena Owens, for their continued putting up with me and my stories.

Thanks goes to, podiatrist, Dr. Joshua Boateng for his insight and suggestions.

I want to thank Lydell Coffer for his unwavering love for my book and for his motivational energy towards my story.

Thank you, also, goes to Robert Nickens, Sr., for being my second reader for my book and for being a great source of encouragement.

To my friends Nick Mundy, Phyllis Brown, Vaughn Greg, Lester Manning, and our English teacher

Valerie Owens

Fred Nichols, thank you for our history at Stetson Junior High School.

To my friend Anajinette Owens, thanks for our days from AFNA (American Foundation for Negro Affairs), in between, and to our now senior years.

I thank you Delores Brown for your unconditional friendship, good words, and advice.

In Arkansas –

At the University of Arkansas Law School in Little Rock, I would like to thank Professor Lynn Foster for giving me a reason to dream again.

I wish to thank the University of Arkansas Writing Center for editing my book.

And, thanks goes to Vinnie Francis who did all my original typing so I would not have to cut off my glamorous fingernails to type it myself.

Everywhere –

Thank you to my friends, associates, acquaintances, and readers for your support and any helpful comments given.

231

America Huh! I'm Going Home

Valerie Owens

.

ABOUT THIS STORY

**This story is not to say that this is the
way it is
in all of Africa or even in all of
Nigeria.
This was my trip to Nigeria and what
happened to me.**

America Huh! I'm Going Home

**Valerie Owens, a graduate
student, age thirty-one, single,
without children, with one semester
left for her Master's, crosses the
Atlantic to Africa with the
"chameleon" Darsalena Eze.**

**Darsalena knew Valerie as the
person who sat beside her at a
graduate school dinner. Their
interaction was based solely upon the
ease of talking to each other. And,
when she asked Valerie to assist her
with research, Darsalena is surprised
to find herself both befriended by and
now connected to Valerie. She likes
their plans to travel to the University,
in Nigeria, Africa where a lot more
emerges.**

**Darsalena's shock over a family
emergency there is equaled only by
her husband's despising of Valerie. A
change in their journey stuns Valerie,
as she is suddenly faced with a
challenging choice. And, she not only
feels abandoned, but, is in danger.**

234

Valerie Owens

Legal issues and some of the ethnic, racial, and cultural differences among Africans and Afro-Americans impact them. She spends twenty-eight days stranded as a woman traveling first with someone that she didn't know very well and then ending up traveling alone. Not reaching her destination, she was forced into homelessness. She went from 165 lbs. to 133 lbs. as a result of the stress from: not having enough to eat; not being able to speak a local language; and being set up to be sold after witnessing two teenagers stoned to death.

AMERICA HUH!
I'M GOING HOME
By VALERIE OWENS

**Pay online by PayPal at website
www.americahuh.com**   **OR**

**Place order by phone:
1-267-255-2976**   **OR**

**Email order to:
ladyjaneowens@hotmail.com**

                       OR

Mail in payment to:

Send to: **Thornbird Publishing
Attn.: Valerie Owens
P.O. Box 153
Jenkintown PA 19046**

Valerie Owens

Shipping Information:

Ship to:

Name

_____

Address_____

City_____

State _____

Zip code _____

Phone number:

Day _____

Evening_____

Quantity   **Price**   **Total**
_____ **X** **$ 15.00 =** _____

Payment type:
[ ] check   **[ ] money order**

Code (if applicable) _____

America Huh! I'm Going Home

____ Autographed Copy Requested

To _____

Message _____

_____

_____

Valerie Owens

Shipping Information:

Ship to:

Name
_____

Address_____

City_____

State _____

Zip code _____

Phone number:

Day _____

Evening_____

Quantity   **Price**   **Total**
_____ X   **$ 15.00 =**   _____

Payment type:
[ ] check   [ ] money order

Code (if applicable) _____
239

America Huh! I'm Going Home

____ **Autographed Copy Requested**

To _____

Message _____

_____

_____._____